And as the garden causeth the things that are
    sown in it to spring forth;
So the Lord God will cause righteousness and praise
    to spring forth before all the nations.

JESUS

the Carpenter's Son

By SOPHIA L. FAHS

With illustrations by
CYRUS LE ROY BALDRIDGE

THE BEACON PRESS • BOSTON

1950

MANUFACTURED IN UNITED STATES OF AMERICA

Foreword

WAS Jesus real or was he just a story person? When he was a baby did he know that he was different from all other babies? Did the angels tell him? Was he surprised when he found out? Could Jesus do anything he wanted to do? Did he die because he wanted to die, or couldn't he help being killed? Why do we call him Jesus Christ? Is Christ his family name? Why do some people say he is "the Son of God"? Does God have only one son? How did they know he was "born King of angels"? Did he have wings? These are questions some boys and girls have asked. They have felt confused.

Have you ever put into words your own wonderings about Jesus? Or have you been afraid to let yourself think clearly about him? Perhaps you have heard stories about Jesus ever since you were in kindergarten, and you are "sick and tired of hearing about him." There are many who can repeat words which they have heard about Jesus but cannot tell what the words mean. They have accepted with little thought what good people have said. They have assumed that the stories told them were just as they are in the Bible, and they have relied upon the Bible as being all true at every point. The young people who will like this book will not be those who are afraid to carry responsibility for their own thoughts.

"But how shall we know if the stories in this book are true?" you ask. I cannot assure you that they are completely true. You need to be prepared to question them. Keep your minds awake as you read. After each chapter ask yourselves: Could this have happened? On what assured facts has the author built up this story? Read for yourselves the verses in the gospel records which are listed at the end of the book as being the background of each story. Use your own imaginations.

Through your own study of history you have by now learned enough about hunting for facts to realize that when one tries to find out about someone who lived a long while ago it is difficult to discover the exact truth. The old records may be scanty. Some may have been lost entirely. Others may have been mutilated. The wording may be vague. Not half of what you wish to know will be told. But you piece together every precious bit of

v

information you can find. When two writers do not agree, you try to decide which is the more trustworthy. You have to choose between them. You search in books which tell about other people living at the same time as the person of whom you wish to know. From these books you learn of the general conditions under which the man lived, the habits and customs of his people, the geography of his home country and a thousand and one other scraps of knowledge — if you can lay your hands upon them.

All these varied pieces of information you gather into some kind of order. You begin trying to imagine yourself as living in that long-ago time. You read between the short lines of the accounts you have found telling about the man until you begin to see him in his home and with his friends. He comes to life as a person.

Ernest Renan, a French author who about seventy-five years ago wrote one of the most interesting books about Jesus ever published, once said: "The historian's talent consists in making a true picture out of features that are of themselves not true." This expresses what I have tried to do in this book. Many of the details in the stories might have happened, but I do not fancy they actually did happen just as I have told them. Yet they are not the kind of details that would have been put into a fairy tale. They have been based upon facts gathered from the study of many books written by scholars. In a large sense, the stories are intended to represent the truth about Jesus. It is hoped that the vivid details added to the brief accounts in the gospels will help to make Jesus real — to bring him to life, as it were, in your imagination, so that you will be emotionally stirred as you surely would have been had you actually seen and heard him.

As you read, you will find some of the stories omitted which you have often heard. Some of these have been omitted simply because you would not like the book to be too long. The more important events have been chosen in order that you may feel the tragic unfolding of the drama of Jesus' life. Others of the stories have been omitted because they are apparently legends or garbled reports of what happened. Some of these are of small importance to a true understanding of the greatness of Jesus. For instance, it does not really matter how or when or where Jesus was born. It is important, however, to know what there was wrong in the life of his day which Jesus thought needed to be changed and how he went about trying to change these things. It is important also to know why it was that he won so many adoring friends while at the same time he was opposed by some of the leading religious men of his country, and finally why he was killed. The drama of his life is woven around these significant matters.

Some of you who read these stories will find that the character of Jesus which is portrayed is strikingly different from the personality which, up to this time, you have revered and loved as Jesus. You may be offended by this new portrait. You may even find reasons, sound and convincing to you, why you should cling to your former picture of Jesus. You should know that many scholars and Christian leaders will disagree heartily with the Jesus presented in this book. You should seek to learn the basis of their positions as well as to find the grounds for the character portrayed here. I have no urge to struggle for that which is not the truth, or to defend any inadequacies or mistakes due to ignorance or lack of insight. I present the book with a deep wish that I could have interpreted more worthily the man whose life has so significantly changed the course of history.

Although it seems presumptuous to compare my effort to that of the great John Bunyan, yet I confess it gave me comfort to find these words in the preface of his *Pilgrim's Progress*. Since they so adequately express my sentiments on turning my writing over to the printer's indelible ink, I give them here:

> "Well, when I had thus put my ends together,
> I showed them others, that I might see whether
> They would condemn them, or them justify;
> And some said, Let them live; some, Let them die;
> Some said, John, print it; others said, Not so;
> Some said, It might do good; others said, No.
>
> Now was I in a strait, and did not see
> Which was the best thing to be done by me:
> At last I thought, Since you are thus divided,
> I print it will; and so the case decided.
> For, thought I, some I see would have it done,
> Though others in that channel do not run:
> To prove, then, who advised for the best,
> Thus I thought fit to put it to the test."

SOPHIA LYON FAHS

April, 1945

CHAPTERS

Table of

Contents

ILLUSTRATIONS

Frontispiece

Acknowledgements

MANY persons have generously contributed their criticisms and suggestions toward the writing of this book. Two well-known living New Testament scholars have helped me directly. To Dr. Henry Burton Sharman, noted teacher of graduate seminars on the teachings of Jesus, I owe a long tutelage in the critical analysis of the gospel records. To Dr. Frederick C. Grant, Professor of New Testament at the Union Theological Seminary, New York City, I am indebted for reading the manuscript with meticulous care, and for his pointing out certain historical inaccuracies all of which I have sought to eliminate. To Dr. Frederick May Eliot, of Boston, I am deeply grateful both for his frank criticisms and for his hearty encouragement.

The following colleagues and friends have read the manuscript and their discriminating criticisms have resulted in important improvements in the book: Ernest W. Kuebler, Raymond B. Johnson, Duncan Howlett, Grace E. Mayer-Oakes, W. Beach Miller, Dorothy T. Spoerl, Florence W. Klaber, Abigail A. Eliot, Elizabeth M. Manwell, Susan M. Andrews, Joshua Liebman, Dorothy Canfield Fisher, Michael Parks and Mrs. Parks, Peggy Pond Church, C. Ivar Hellstrom, Margaret D. Edwards, Elsie M. Bush and Abbie Lyon Sharman.

Others of my colleagues have helped greatly by using the stories in manuscript form with their church-school classes. I feel a special indebtedness to the boys and girls who so willingly played the role of "book critics." Their candid remarks and the reports of their discussions, as written by their teachers, have been most helpful.

I wish also to express my indebtedness to all those scholarly writers on the life and teachings of Jesus to whose books I have turned for enlightenment.

Neither wide reading nor the generous co-operation of friends, however, should be taken to mean that there is agreement among us regarding the true nature of the picture of Jesus. For better or for worse, the author must accept responsibility for what is written.

SOPHIA LYON FAHS

NEW YORK CITY
April, 1945

JESUS

the Carpenter's Son

"Is not this the carpenter's son? Is not
his mother called Mary? and his brethren,
James, and Joseph, and Simon, and Judas?
And his sisters, are they not all with us?"

— MATTHEW 13:55, 56

All jumped to their feet
and looked out over the
wide plain

CHAPTER 1

The Young Patriots

LATE one afternoon on a rocky ledge overlooking the white flat roofs of the town of Nazareth sat five Jewish boys. They squirmed restlessly as they talked, now and then picking up loose pieces of rock and throwing them down the hillside. Zadok, the weaver's boy; Joash, the stonemason's son; David, the son of a shepherd; Zebedee, the potter's son; and Jesus, son of Joseph the carpenter, made up the group.

These five boys had secretly banded together. They called themselves *Young Patriots*. Like all boys everywhere whose fathers plot and fight to free their countries from bondage to a foreign power, these boys also were determined to fight for their country's

3

liberty. Jesus was their latest recruit. The others had trusted him with their secret. They had begged him to join. They needed a boy with a mind like his. And Jesus was fascinated by their enthusiasm. He wanted to be at something worth while, but he was not sure he wanted to be a Young Patriot. He was feeling his way.

Zebedee and Zadok were the leaders. Just as soon as their parents would let them, they said, they were going to fight. They liked to sit together and dream of what they would do when they were men. They were going to be guerrillas. They would carry knives hidden in their garments. They would hide in caves and come out only at nighttime to plunder gardens and fields, to break into Roman armories to carry off money and swords. Then finally, when there were enough armed guerrillas, they would start a great rebellion and drive the hated Romans from the land.

Yes, this was what these Young Patriots were dreaming of doing when they were men. Zebedee's father was already hiding with a rebel band somewhere among the rocky cliffs across the Lake of Galilee. Zadok's father had fought with the great Judah when his guerrillas raided Sepphoris, a town only six miles from where the boys were then sitting. Zadok had heard the whole exciting story from his father's own lips. The young fellow had told it over and over to the other boys: how the guerrillas had broken into the fortress on the hill and had run off with hundreds of Roman swords and spears; how they had stolen many bags full of money, and had successfully escaped; and how later they had gone secretly in and out of many towns of Galilee, robbing and killing not only Romans but anyone they suspected of being a traitor. Even though the boys at that time were but small children, they remembered sharing the excitement and fear they had felt in the people around them.

Then came the even more terrible experience of seeing for themselves the bloody revenge the Romans took on the Jews because of this daring rebellion. From the very hilltop on which the boys were sitting, they had watched for hours on end the black clouds of smoke rising in the northern horizon over the town of Sepphoris as a Roman army burned it to ashes. Had not these boys also stood through one whole afternoon watching the sorrowful procession of homeless men, women and children trudging along the main highway, with Roman guards marching beside them? The boys could never forget the terror-stricken faces of mothers, the pitiful sobs of children, the proud, sullen bearing of young men, and the agonizing prayers of the old and feeble. Some of the rebels who had first taken part in the raid of Sepphoris had been neighbors in Nazareth. The boys knew them by name. They could never forget the stories they had heard of the tortures these men endured when they were finally captured. How Judah himself escaped the Roman spies no one ever dared to tell.

The Young Patriots were reminded of all these happenings every time they met on the hilltop to talk of what they would do when they were men. They were not the kind to be made afraid, nor would they endure dishonor with patience. They would fight to the death for freedom.

"On my next birthday I'm going to join the rebels. I promise God I will," said Zebedee solemnly one day. "Judah, the son of Hezekiah, is the greatest man in all Galilee. I'm for him with everything I have."

"Don't be in such a hurry, Zebedee," said Zadok. "Judah has failed. We need a stronger deliverer than he. I'm going to wait for the real Messiah[1]— the one God will send down on the clouds. He'll be as strong as a thousand men put together. He'll destroy our enemies with the breath of his mouth."

"That's a wild dream!" put in David. "Who ever heard of a warrior with breath like fire?"

"Rabbi Solomon read us about this Messiah in school yesterday," said Zadok. "Have you forgotten so soon?"

"It's a kind of dream, nevertheless," insisted Jesus. "For hundreds of years our prophets have been dreaming dreams about a

[1]Messiah is the Hebrew word for the expected national leader, whom, it is believed, God will send to the earth.

Messiah. Daniel had his dreams, and Isaiah his, and Enoch and Esdras had theirs. But none of these dreams have come true."

"But," broke in Zebedee again, "Rabbi Solomon said these were God's dreams for the Jewish people and they would surely come true. He was sure of that."

"They can't all come true," said Jesus, "for the dreams are not all alike."

"Well, I hope God sends some kind of a Messiah soon," said Joash. He rose and walked nervously round and round the hilltop as he talked. "I'm sick of all these stories of killing and stoning and burning. It's time the Romans suffered some of the cruelties they've done to us."

"That's the way to talk," said Zebedee. "I want to see every Roman palace burned and every Roman garden overgrown with thorns. I want to see nettles and thistles cover the ruins of their fortresses. I want their homes to become dens of howling wolves and jackals. Yes, I want Isaiah's dream to come true and the sooner the better."

By this time all the boys were moving about restlessly, and all were trying to talk at once.

"There is something evil in these dreams," cried Jesus. "I can't believe they are God's dreams."

"You wouldn't dare say that before Rabbi Solomon!" said Joash. "He'd put you out of the House of Meeting and tell you never to come back."

"And you're not going to be a very good Patriot either," snapped Zebedee. "I can see that."

Just at that moment one of the boys shouted, "Look! Turn around!" All jumped to their feet and looked out over the wide plain that stretched out below them.

"It's a caravan on its way to the sea!"

"Look at the big bags on the camels' humps!"

"They'll go to the town well for water!"

"Let's run!"

These exclamations were scarcely out of the boys' mouths when all five were rushing pell-mell down the hillside toward the great highway that wound its way through the plain. When once the boys had caught up with the caravan, it was not hard for them to keep pace with the slow, easygoing walk of the camels. Yet it seemed no time at all until they were in the town, standing beside the well.

The boys stood about with keen eyes for everything that happened — the drivers bending over the well to drink, and scooping up the water with their hands; their skilled unloading of the burdens from the camels' backs; the camels one by one drinking at the trough; their lanky legs and funny way of kneeling; their lazy-looking eyes. Not one of these sights did the boys miss. How they wished they might be allowed to sit on top of the camels' humps! But they were afraid to ask. Instead they tried to talk politely with the strange drivers.

"Sir," said Zebedee, stepping up to one of the older men, "how long have the camels been without water?"

But the man answered only with a blank look and a jumble of queer sounds.

The other boys all laughed. "He's talking Greek," said Joash. "No, it's Phoenician, I think, but I can't tell what he said."

"Maybe it's Babylonian," suggested David.

"What country have you come from?" Jesus ventured next.

"And where are you going?"

"And what kinds of things are you carrying in those bags?"

All these questions came popping out one after the other. But the men would shake their heads or try to make signs with their hands or burst out in some unknown language. It was fun for the boys to guess the answers to their own questions. They felt, as they looked and listened, that they were having a peep into a new and excitingly big world which some day they would like to see.

How long the boys had been there at the well none of them realized, until suddenly they were startled by the blowing of the evening trumpet from the roof of the House of Meeting. Could it really be that the sun had gone down? The boys knew then that they must run home at once for supper and evening prayers.

.   .   .   .

That night after the evening meal, Joseph, the carpenter, said to his oldest son: "Come with me up the hill to the garden patch before it is dark. I need your help."

"Gladly, sir!" said Jesus, and he proudly started off at his father's side.

It took but a short while to pick the vegetables needed for the next day's meals. Then Joseph said, "Let us sit down on the grass for a while. It is cooler here than in our courtyard." This was just what Jesus had been hoping for. He spread himself full length on the grass as his father sat down beside him.

"Father, did you know," said Jesus, "that I was wishing I could talk with you tonight?"

"No, Son, but I do recall now that you had little to say this evening at the supper table, even about the camels. Did the drivers abuse you or bring you bad news?"

"No, Father, it's another matter that troubles me," said Jesus. "Most of the boys I know are afraid to talk to their fathers. I guess there isn't another father like you in all Nazareth."

"Perhaps there isn't another son like you who bothers his head about so many questions," said Joseph with a smile. "You should have had a rabbi for a father." He paused for a moment to catch the sparkle in Jesus' eye, then he added more seriously, "It is well that you are sometimes troubled, Son. You have been born in a time of great disgrace and sorrow for our people."

Jesus did not answer for a moment, but lay looking up dreamily at the blue clouds. Finally he sat up straight and began to unload his questions.

"Was there as much fighting and killing when you were a boy, Father, as there is now?"

"Sometimes I think there was more, Son. You know I grew up under the rule of Herod the Great. It would be hard to imagine a king who could be more cruel than he."

"Did you ever do any fighting yourself, Father?"

"No, Son, I never carried a sword, but I have watched the results of fighting by others. I've seen homes burned down and whole families left to beg — without a place to lay their heads."

"Such things are still happening, Father."

Joseph went on as if he had not heard Jesus' remark. "I remember one black Passover as if it were only yesterday. It was a beautiful spring. I had gone as usual down to Jerusalem to attend the festival. You were just a small child then, Jesus. Thousands, yes, ten of thousands of pilgrims filled the big city and crowded the wide temple courts."

"You'll take me with you the next time you go to Jerusalem, won't you, Father?" Jesus interrupted excitedly.

"Yes, Jesus, but I hope you won't see such a sight as I saw that year," said Joseph. "Our people always become excited when we celebrate the day of our freedom from the Egyptians. But that year our excitement was not one of happiness. The Romans had required us all to register in order to be taxed. We were furious. Men came with knives and cudgels, even into the temple court itself. They shouted defiance against the Romans. The armed Roman soldiers from the castle rushed down upon the crowd and killed them right and left. The blood of over a thousand worshipers was spilled that day on the marble pavements of the temple!"

"Were you in the crowd, Father?" asked Jesus in alarm.

"No, not then, but later, in the darkness of the night, when the fighting was over, I went with a few others into the temple court. We walked about among the dead in search of the wounded. I helped carry them to places of safety where their wounds could be dressed. Many of the rebels who had escaped, however, were later captured. Some days after, I saw their bodies hanging from wooden crosses outside the city walls. That is a horrible memory. It haunts me over and over."

"Oh, Father!" cried Jesus as he covered his face between his knees. "Wait! Do not tell me more just now."

For a long while the two sat in silence. They could not find words strong enough to carry their feelings of horror.

Finally Jesus broke the quiet. "Father, why have you never joined the guerrillas so that you could fight, too?"

"It's been hard to know what to do, Son. I love my country, and often I have been filled with bitter hate. But when I stop to reason with myself, I know that it is useless for us to fight the Romans now. They are much too strong for us. Every rebellion ends in defeat. Rebels are killed and nothing is gained. Some day I believe the Messiah will come. He will be strong enough to deliver us from the hands of our enemies. I have decided to wait as patiently as I can for him to lead us."

"But how long must we wait, Father?" cried Jesus. "What if the Messiah never comes?"

"Do not speak so carelessly, Son. We must have faith. The rabbis say that if everyone in the nation would obey God's laws perfectly, even for one day, the Messiah would come. The important thing for us to do, then, is not to go about hating and killing our enemies. Instead we should live day by day honestly and justly with our neighbors and be faithful in doing all that God has commanded us. The rest we can leave to God. Our reward is sure."

All the while as he talked, Jesus looked wonderingly into his father's stern eyes. He surely was no coward. Neither was Zebedee's father a coward. But how different the two men were! Which one did Jesus wish to follow? The others wanted to be like Zebedee's father and fight. If Jesus told them he was not going to fight, would the boys jeer at him? Was there no other way of being a Young Patriot?

Jesus wished he could tell his father about the secret society. Perhaps his father could help him. But Jesus had promised not to tell. So the two walked home talking of other things.

There was no use arguing the matter with the other Young Patriots, either, until his own thoughts were clearer. So he kept his ponderings hidden away as seeds are kept in the ground.

2 A New Thought Grows

"CHILDREN, obey your parents in the Lord." No Jewish child of Jesus' day ever doubted his duty on this point. He took obedience for granted just as he accepted the clothes he was given to wear. It was simpler that way, when large families were crowded into small rooms and everyone had to help with the work. All this was surely true of the home where Jesus lived. Like an oblong block built of stones, it stood against the hillside with its front door opening directly on the narrow paved street. When Jesus was but a small child, there had been only one room in the house, with the carpenter shop alongside, also opening on the street. But now that the family had grown so large, his father Joseph had built a second room back of the first.

Fortunately, there was a flat roof with a low wall around it and a stairway leading up from the outside, so that the children could climb up there and play in the sunshine. Behind the house was an open space, where an old fig tree spread its welcome shade and where a couple of goats frisked about as freely as they could, in spite of being tied to the tree. In this open court a stone and mud fireplace had been built and there the family's meals were often cooked. With no chimney or stove in the house, this was a great advantage.

Even with two rooms, this plain little house was now full to overflowing with children. Besides Jesus, the oldest, four brothers had been born one after the other — James and Joseph and Simon and Judas — and there were two sisters, also. Except in the warm summer when some of the family spent the night on the roof, they all slept side by side on mats on the floor — except the baby. For her the father had built a wooden boxlike crib.

When morning came they all rolled up their sleeping mats and stored them away in a niche in the wall. This one room then became a dining-room and general living-room. It was furnished with only the barest necessities, such as a small low table, a few small rugs scattered on the hard clay floor, and a couple of chests where Sabbath-day clothes were neatly folded away and kept clean and safe. In the other room was the kitchen, where meals were cooked over an open fireplace in the middle of the floor. It was also a storage room; large water jugs stood against the wall, with empty basins and smaller pitchers on a shelf above them. In one corner stood tall bins full of grain. From the rafters hung strings of dried figs and pomegranates.

For Jesus, in a house so full of other children, there were few quiet daytime moments. Always there was baby in her box crib cooing or crying for milk, or little sister toddling everywhere at his heels, or Judas begging for things and asking questions, or James and Joseph and Simon wanting their older brother to do something or other.

With so large a family there was also much work to be done. The two goats had to be milked, and the wood gathered and chopped for the fire. There was grain to be ground between millstones, and meal to be mixed with oil and rolled out in flat cakes and baked over the open fire in the courtyard. There was also the butter to be made; a queer-looking goatskin bag was filled with milk and hung from a pole where it could be swung back and forth until the curds were separated out and the butter came. Every day Jesus' mother, Mary, would sweep the much-used floors with her small broom and spread out the little rugs to sit on. There were clothes to be patched and new garments to be sewn. Every day there were meals to be cooked, dried fish to be fried, or meat and vegetables to be boiled over the open fire; and every morning the little lamps had to be trimmed and filled with oil.

Beside all this, every drop of water the family used for drinking or washing had to be carried in jugs from the town well and poured into the large jars standing in the storage room. With great admiration, Jesus often watched his mother as she walked back over the cobblestones of the narrow street, keeping her head high and balancing the big jar of water on top of it.

Jesus often experimented in the courtyard to see if he, too, could balance a jar of water on his head, and he was proud when at last he succeeded in keeping it steady while he walked all the way across the court. But Jesus soon learned that certain kinds of work were called "women's work," and certain other kinds of work were called "men's work." His mother said to him, "You must learn to do the things your father does, for you are a man."

So Jesus already had become his father's regular assistant in the carpenter shop. Here he would labor sometimes the whole day through, for now he could handle the saw and hammer with skill, and his father let him take responsibility for measuring boards the right lengths and widths for doors and doorframes, and for shaping the end pieces of ploughs and rakes so that they were both sharp and strong.

Once Jesus had gone with his father into the orchard outside the town and had helped to cut off a branch from an old olive tree.

On his own shoulder he had carried home one of the sawed logs. Joseph liked to have his oldest son learning to work as a man, and Jesus enjoyed having his father expect difficult things from him; but sometimes it was hard not to wish for more time to go exploring with the other boys of the neighborhood. Jesus liked to play in the market place and to dance to the music of his cousin's pipe. He liked to wander alone through the wooded fields to hunt for turtles in the brook, or to listen to the songs of birds. Nor was it always easy to get away when the Young Patriots called a meeting in the grove on the hilltop. Yet even while he worked in the carpenter shop alongside his father, exciting things happened sometimes, and Jesus learned much that he was curious to know.

One day, for example, Ezra, the father of Joash, came to the shop to order a new yoke for his oxen. When he had finished his business, he began talking with Joseph, almost in a whisper as if he were telling him a secret. Jesus stopped his sawing in order not to miss a word. Ezra told of the guerrilla band that was hiding near the shore of the Lake of Galilee. One of their messengers, he said, had just been in Nazareth, secretly trying to enlist recruits. Finally, thumping his fist on the carpenter's bench, Ezra fairly shouted, "I tell you, I'm going to join the guerrillas in a few days myself."

"Don't be foolish, Ezra," pleaded Joseph. "The Romans are too powerful. A horrible death is the sure fate of anyone who is so rash as to take up the sword against them."

"How do you know, Joseph? Galilee is full of guerrillas. They say that there are over five thousand armed men in Galilee alone ready to fight."

"But what are they against the Roman legions?" said Joseph. "Have you so soon forgotten the story of Sepphoris? God's time has not yet come. I tell you, when it comes God will send us a Messiah who will have the strength of ten thousand men. He will destroy our enemies with the fiery breath of his mouth. Then we can be bold, but not now."

"But perhaps our Messiah is already here among us," Ezra insisted. "God's time must be near. We can't expect God to help us until we do something ourselves. Some of us have got to be ready to die."

With these words the man walked out the door. Jesus began sawing again, with quick, strong movements. He, too, wished he could do something for his country. But before he could turn his thoughts into words his father would understand, another customer entered the shop. So Jesus' wonderings could only go round and round in his own mind. What if the guerrilla bands suddenly appeared in Nazareth? What if they should send a spy to kill the Roman captain? Would a Roman army pounce down on Nazareth as they had on Sepphoris so short a while before and burn their own town to ashes? Or would the Messiah come first? Would this Messiah come before Jesus would be old enough to join a guerrilla band? What would the Messiah do? Jesus wished to know what his father thought, but there seemed to be so few times even in his father's shop when they could talk things through.

So it was a red-letter day when Jesus was able to go off alone with his father to work on the small plot of land the family owned on the hillside back of the house. There they had a garden of vegetables and a field of grain and a small vineyard. It was a fresh, clear morning in late October. For some days the autumn rains had been falling, and the earth, which had been baked hard by the hot summer sun, was now soft enough to plough. Joseph wished to get his field planted.

When the plow had been well harnessed to the yoke between the oxen, Joseph took hold of the wooden handle saying, "I will do the plowing, Jesus, and you may guide the oxen back and forth over the field."

When they had finished preparing the field, Joseph handed Jesus a bag full of barley seeds, saying, "Today you may try your hand at sowing the seed."

Proudly Jesus tied the open bag to his girdle so that he could reach it. With easy, strong steps he walked barefoot down the plowed land, and back. All the while he sang a song, partly with words and partly without, as with wide sweeps of his arm out and back, out and back, he scattered the seeds through his fingers.

Never had Jesus known quite the joy that came to him then. The broken soil seemed to change into a place of wonder, and the brown specks he was scattering upon it became living gifts more precious than silver, direct from the hands of the Creator.

When the planting was finished, he and his father sat in the shade of the old olive tree, and ate a lunch of bread and honey. Before their eyes rose range upon range of hills, green shading into a soft blue like the sky. The hilltops seemed to reach the horizon. Below them spread rolling meadows newly washed with rain, while, above, fleecy grey clouds speckled the sky. It was a day for dreaming and stretching one's thoughts.

Words of Isaiah, which he had learned the day before in the village school, came to Jesus' mind. He said them aloud, almost as if he were alone.

> For as the earth bringeth forth her bud,
> And as the garden causeth the things that are sown in
>   it to spring forth;
> So the Lord God will cause righteousness and praise to
>   spring forth before all the nations.

There was the wonder of growing in these words of Isaiah like the wonder Jesus felt when he was scattering the seeds. But Isaiah was not thinking of seeds a man could scatter through his fingers. Isaiah was thinking of goodness growing from small beginnings.

Surely that was what God's Messiah should be for — to bring goodness. But this was not at all what the Young Patriots talked about. They talked of fighting and killing and of a Messiah who would come suddenly in the clouds. Daniel had imagined a

us brought his sleeping
t up on the roof

-B-

Messiah like that. The guerrillas talked that way, too. They said there was no chance for a just and peaceful world until the Romans were crushed. When the Jewish Messiah ruled the world he would make men do right. But Jesus was doubtful. Could people be made good by armies and swords? Was God going to frighten the world into a friendly brotherhood by sending some terrible catastrophe? Or was Isaiah right in thinking that there was a little kingdom, like a heaven on earth, wherever there was a person who let the goodness in him grow quietly, naturally, as seeds grow. Who was right? Which was God's kingdom? Jesus could no longer keep his questions to himself.

"Father," he asked, "how do you think the Kingdom of God is going to come? Is the Kingdom going to come suddenly with the Messiah coming down out of the sky, flashing fire out of his mouth to destroy our enemies first? Or is it going to grow slowly and quietly as seeds grow in a garden, without our knowing at first that it's growing at all?"

Joseph looked at Jesus with a quick glance of surprise. Joseph was reminded of what he himself had said in the shop to Ezra, the father of Joash: "The Messiah will destroy our enemies with the fiery breath of his mouth." At that time Joseph, too, had been quoting Isaiah. He had never before thought of these two sayings together. Sometimes he wished his son would not trouble him with so many questions. Finally, he answered: "Son, you should leave questions like that to the teachers to answer. All I know is that some day God's Chosen One will rule the world, and justice and goodness will fill the earth as the waters cover the sea."

That night Jesus brought his sleeping mat up to the roof. As he lay watching the stars shine out one after the other until the clear, dark sky was spangled with lights, he tried to imagine a dazzling angel flying down, and entering the houses of the Romans to kill the people in them by his fiery breath.

But somehow such an angel did not seem to fit the peaceful,

twinkling sky and the quiet town of sleeping people. The stars themselves seemed almost to flash back to him the words of Isaiah:

> As the garden causeth the things that are sown in it to
>   spring forth;
> So the Lord God will cause righteousness and praise to
>   spring forth before all the nations.

As Jesus said these words over and over, they seemed to belong to the real world where goodness did grow like seeds, quietly and slowly. He thought again of Zadok and Joash, of David and Zebedee, the other Young Patriots. What would they think of this new idea of his? If he tried to explain it to them, would they call him soft — a childish dreamer of dreams who didn't know what he was talking about? He began to feel that some day he would have to tell the boys that he could no longer belong to their society. If he really believed in this new kind of a Kingdom, it wouldn't be honest to pretend he didn't. Jesus could see the disdain in the boys' faces. He felt himself cringing under their taunts. "You're a coward and afraid to fight," that's what they would say. What did he really think, anyway?

With these thoughts wrestling back and forth in his mind, Jesus finally fell asleep.

3 A First Visit to the Great City

On a soft, warm evening early the following April, Jesus was walking home with his father and carrying in his arms the first stalks of ripened barley from their small field. Coming to the low doorway of their home, Joseph touched his finger to the little box fastened to the doorpost. It was a holy box because inside was a little scroll with some words from the Holy Law written on it. Joseph kissed the finger that had touched the holy box and then said a prayer. "God preserve our going out and our coming in. Amen." His son, coming up behind, also touched the holy box and kissed his finger and prayed the very same words.[1]

Mother and children, waiting inside, heard their voices and rose to greet them. "Good husband," said Mary, "Peace be to you." "And may peace be yours, my beloved," said Joseph.

With a smile of gladness, Jesus handed his mother the stalks of barley. "They are the very first that are ripe. May I take the barley grain with me to Jerusalem?"

Mary took the stalks and sang as she did so, "Blessed art thou, O God of the world, who givest us our harvests." Soon all the family were humming the song as they prepared for supper.

James brought a basin of water so that Jesus and his father might wash their feet. Simon brought a second basin and passed it to each one in turn until their hands also were washed. One of the daughters lighted two lamps and set them on the low supper table.

Father sat at the end with his oldest son on his right hand and his other children seated about him in the order of their ages. Then, taking a round, flat loaf of bread, the father broke it and, bowing his head, he said a prayer of thanksgiving. As long as Jesus could remember, his father had said these very same words every evening when the family sat down to supper. The mother then brought a big bowl of green vegetables from the fire, some goat's milk, a jar of honey, and a few figs that had grown on the tree in the courtyard. They all ate and drank heartily for they were hungry after a long day.

Later in the evening when the other children were asleep on

---

[1]The name given to this holy box is Mezuza.

their mats, Jesus and his father sat alone together on the roof top. The street below was quiet and dark except for the flickering of small lights through open doorways. Above, the stars shone so big and bright in the dark sky that it seemed almost as though Jesus could reach out his hands and touch the stars with his fingers. In the quiet dark he felt somehow close to God, as if he were praying even though he was not saying a word. His thoughts were like a secret between himself and God. It was so different from the way he had felt when he had been listening to his father praying at the supper table.

At last Jesus broke the stillness. "Father, why is it that you always say the same words every night when you pray?"

"You are a strange boy to ask such a question, Jesus. I say the words that my teacher taught me when I went to the school in the meetinghouse. Did you not also learn this prayer at school?"

"Yes, but Father, don't you sometimes feel like saying your own words or maybe like being quiet and not saying words at all?"

"Son, the words I would think of myself would be too simple and common to use before the Almighty. They would seem foolish. Better keep to the things you've been taught, or you will get yourself into trouble."

"When I go to Jerusalem with you day after tomorrow to the great festival in the temple," asked Jesus, scarcely hearing his father's warning, "will there be someone there who can answer my questions?"

"There are wise teachers in Jerusalem certainly, but they will not have time for a boy like you."

"But I want to be a teacher myself some day, Father. I want to go to school where there are teachers who can help me work out for myself what is right and what is wrong."

"Don't be so ambitious, Son. You are only a carpenter's boy and a farmer from Galilee. Those learned teachers in Jerusalem may not pay any attention to you."

"But ——"

"It's time for bed now, Jesus. Good night! God bless you and keep you." So Jesus obeyed his father's word and went off down the stairs to bed.

Later when Mary came upstairs to the roof to be with her husband, he said to her, "What do you think our oldest son was saying today?" Then Joseph told her the conversation he and Jesus had had earlier in the evening. Joseph and Mary sat silently a long while, each wondering what their boy would do when he was grown; while Jesus, down below with the other children of the household, was sleeping and dreaming.

.   .   .   .

Each year in April, Jesus' father, along with all the other faithful Jewish fathers of Nazareth, had been accustomed to make the trip to the capital city of Jerusalem, some seventy miles away, to celebrate the great yearly festival called the Passover. This year it had been decided that Jesus might go, too, since he was now twelve years old. His mother also had been persuaded to go along. A good neighbor offered to take care of the other children while the party was gone.

Jesus realized that he was soon to see things new and strange. His father had often tried to describe the temple. He had told of its great courts open to the sky, of the column of fire and smoke always rising from the great stone altar standing before the most holy place — the golden house where the invisible God of earth and sky had chosen to dwell. His father had told of the animals whose blood was poured out upon the altar, of the gifts of wine and meal and first fruits that the people brought. He had told of the white-robed choirs who sang while musicians played on harps and flutes. He had told of the priests who called with their loud-voiced trumpets and of the crowds falling down on their knees and bowing their heads to the ground before the invisible One. Joseph had told also of the teachers who sat among the pillars in the cloisters, and, between the ceremonies, taught the people who came to listen to them. Jesus had tried to imagine what it would all be like, but his mother would say, "You will have to wait and see for yourself."

All over Nazareth, mothers had been busy for weeks making gay new clothes for the pilgrims to wear. Some had carefully mended old garments that had lain stored away in chests unused since the last Passover festival. They had ground and saved small measures of meal made from the first ripe barley and wheat. They had dried figs and made wine from the first grapes, and oil from the first ripe olives. They had dried many kinds of herbs that would give off a sweet smell when burned on the altar of incense. These fruits of their gardens they had packed in baskets to be taken to the temple.

All through the winter, Jesus' family had kept a little lamb in the courtyard along with the two goats that gave them milk. Jesus and his brothers, with special pains, had fed and cared for this lamb because it had been bought for a special honor. The lamb was to be taken to the temple and its life blood was to be given as the family gift to the Almighty. Often the boys had playfully frisked with the lamb around the courtyard. Many an afternoon Jesus had taken it, and the two goats, up to the hilltop north of Nazareth where they could feed freely among the grasses while he would sit and play his flute.

Finally, the great morning dawned when the happy pilgrims were to start forth on their way. Before daylight the big crowd began to gather in the village market place. There were donkeys, heavily loaded with tents and bundles of provisions for the days of camping along the way. Women came in their bright-colored dresses, trimmed with dangling beads. On their heads they jauntily carried the precious baskets of first fruits they had prepared. Zebedee, Joash, David, Zadok and Jesus all came running up the street, each with his own lamb on a tether. There were many other boys beside. Some were old enough to go as pilgrims. Others were there merely to see the sights.

As the procession passed down through the village streets and out into the open country beyond, the singing of the pilgrims could be heard all over the town. At the head of the procession were the flute players. David and Jesus were the only boy musicians among them. Altogether the pilgrims from Nazareth made a big company of over a hundred people.

At each new town through which they passed, they met more pilgrims ready to go to Jerusalem. Jesus had never before seen so many people. Day after day, for three full days they walked, uphill and down, beside fields gay with many-colored flowers and into deep canyons shaded even at midday. Jesus had never before been so far away from home. When each day's march was ended and the animals had been fed and meals cooked and eaten, Jesus had to admit that he was tired and ready to rest. But he was never too sleepy to listen for a while to the storytellers, and to play his flute as the crowds sang over and over the old songs everybody knew.

Finally, on the morning of the fourth day, the pilgrims came upon a hilltop from which they could see the city of their dreams. Across a deep valley, on a lower hill, the great walls of the city stood with the white marble temple rising above them like a crown. Although Jesus had often been told of the great outer court whose massive walls outlined the entire hill, he had not been able to imagine how big it could be. Nor had he been able to picture such beauty in a building — walled courts within walled courts, each rising higher than the one outside it. The golden roof of the inner-most shrine in the center, high above all the rest, shone like a gleaming gem in the sky.

"How beautiful are thy courts, O Lord," sang the people as they stood looking. "Blessed is he that cometh in the name of the Lord."

On a hillside outside the city wall, the Nazareth party set up camp and built open fireplaces where they might cook and where the Passover lambs might be roasted when the great day of the feast

came. With so much work to be done, it was not until the following day that they were able to join the other pilgrims in the great
city.

Early the next morning, Jesus and his parents worked their way
through the great gate in the north wall of the city, up a noisy,
crowded street and across a bridge that led to the temple. Joseph
was carrying a bag of fine flour across his shoulder. It was to be
given as a prayer for forgiveness. Mary carried on her head a basket
full of the first fruits she had dried. These she was bringing as a
prayer of thanksgiving. In one hand, Jesus carried a small bowl of
the meal he had made from the stalks of barley gathered in the field.
By the other hand he was leading his year-old-lamb — the household pet — the animal he had fed and played with all the winter.
This was the family's great gift; a token of their devotion to the God
of Israel.

Thousands of other worshipers crowded along beside them,
many also leading their lambs. Some were carrying doves in their
arms. Everyone had a gift of some kind. None came empty handed
into the House of the Almighty. As Jesus walked in the midst
of the crowd a strange new feeling came over him. It was partly
gladness and partly pain. He felt part of something great and large.
He, too, was eager to pay homage to the Unseen Giver of all good
things, but this new way of worshiping seemed strange and he was
not sure he cared for it.

As they neared the outer gate of the temple the stone walls and
towers rose high before them. Pushed along by the crowds, Jesus
walked through the open gate into a stately hall between rows of
high pillars and then on into an open, sunny court beyond. Jesus
had supposed that everyone would become quiet, once they were
inside the temple wall. He had expected them to stand in an or-
derly way and listen to prayers and songs as the people did in the
meetinghouse in Nazareth. Instead he was shocked to find himself in a noisy market place! All sorts of things useful in the cere-

monies were for sale — incense, sweet herbs, meal, jars of wine, fruits and doves. Booths and stalls were all about and the people were bargaining over prices just as they did on the streets.

White-robed priests stood in rows here and there. They were taking the gifts the people were bringing. Mary gave her basket of first fruits to one of them. Joseph handed another his bag of fine flour. Jesus gave another his bowl of barley meal. As for their precious lamb, it had to be examined by one of the priests before it could be presented for sacrifice. Jesus watched anxiously as the priest felt its woolly body from head to feet to see if he could find a scar or fault of any kind. Even when the man had pronounced it perfect, Joseph had to pay half a shekel for the priest's services. What did the priest do with the money? Jesus wondered.

When all these matters had been attended to, the family pushed its way forward up the steps and through the beautiful doors of shining brass that led into the next and higher court. They dropped their gifts of money into silver bowls placed there for that purpose. Before them at the farther end of this court, at the top of steps leading to a still higher court, stood a choir of white-robed men singing songs of thanksgiving. Jesus began to feel at last that he was in a house of prayer. But what was going on in that higher court beyond? He could not see clearly over the heads of the crowds.

Presently two white-robed priests standing in this open doorway blew three blasts on their silver trumpets. The crowd that had filled the upper court began coming down. Then the Nazareth family and others in the court below were given their turn to move up. Leaving Mary behind in the lower court, Jesus followed his father up the steps and into the higher court. Beyond a railing on a still higher level he could see the long stone altar on which a fire was burning. Two lines of white-robed priests stood waiting to serve the worshipers.

Jesus followed his father as he led the lamb through an open gate at the side of the court and gave it over to another priest.

Jesus saw his father lay his hand solemnly on the lamb's head while the priest prayed. Then the dreaded moment came. Jesus did not see clearly how it happened, but he knew that his lamb had been killed. He saw a priest hold a silver bowl beneath its bleeding throat and solemnly carry the bowl of blood back toward the railing and up the steps to the high altar. There with a branch of hyssop[1] he sprinkled some of the blood upon the altar, then poured the rest out upon the stones. Jesus also saw another priest bring part of the lamb's body up to the altar and lay it upon the fire.

As Jesus stood watching the burning pile, the choir began to sing. He tried to join with the others in chanting a psalm of thankfulness, but the words came from his mouth as sounds without meaning. These bloody sacrifices seemed strange to him. He wondered: Did the Lord of the world, the Creator of all living creatures, really like such gifts of blood? As he looked about on the faces of the men about him, he asked himself: Does no one else question these things?

Dazed by all he had seen, Jesus turned to leave the court of sacrifice. His father, carrying the limp body of the lamb flung over his shoulder, beckoned his son to follow.

. . . .

That evening on a hillside outside the city wall, Jesus and his parents and a group of friends and relatives sat around an open fire. With many prayers and much singing, they feasted upon the roast lamb. It was a solemn meal, for they all felt they had shared the life blood of the lamb with God. It was also a merrymaking feast with jokes and laughter, and lasted long into the night. Jesus joined in the celebration, doing just what his parents had taught him as well as he knew how. As he again took up his flute and played while the others sang, his heart grew lighter. He felt himself among happy friends.

The next morning, Jesus was determined to go back to the

[1] A small plant like mint and with little blue flowers.

temple, but this time he did not go to watch the sacrificing of animals. He went rather in search of the teachers — those rabbis he had so often been told about — who sat in the cloisters among the pillars away from the noisy crowds, talking to those who cared to listen. On finding such a group, Jesus sat down and listened, too. He was amazed at the things the teachers knew, and at the ready answers they gave to the questions people asked. At last Jesus was having the chance for which he had been longing. He found courage now and then to ask a question himself. For the first two times, Joseph or Mary went with Jesus, but each morning after that he went alone and, for several hours at a time, he would sit listening or asking questions.

Finally, the great week was ended and the day came when Joseph and Mary and their company from Nazareth were to start home. By that time, the parents had grown so accustomed to letting Jesus go his own way that they started off with the others, assuming that Jesus was with some of the neighbors. When night came, however, they looked for their son all over the camp. They grew worried because they could not find him anywhere.

With anxious hearts, the parents walked back to Jerusalem the next morning going from house to house where they had been at one time or another during their stay, but no Jesus was to be found. Finally, they decided to look for him in the temple. How astonished they were when, entering one of the cloisters among the pillars, they saw their son, sitting quietly, with older men all around him, listening to the rabbi! They heard Jesus ask a question. They trembled lest the teacher become annoyed by their son. But the teacher listened with interest and answered the boy's question respectfully, and Jesus was all absorbed in what the teacher was saying.

Presently Jesus looked around and noticed his parents standing by the doorway watching him. He stepped out of the hall to speak with them.

Jesus sat down and listened, too

"Son, why have you behaved like this?" asked Mary. "Your father and I have been looking anxiously for you."

"Mother, why have you been looking for me all over the city? Did you not know that I would be right here in the temple?"

But the parents could not understand their son. They told him he would have to go home with them at once, for the rest of the party were already on their way.

So Jesus' dream of being with the great teachers to listen and to ask them questions came to an end. Soon he would be called a man and allowed to decide things for himself, but not yet.

4 Meeting the Hermit Preacher

ONE by one the years had come and gone for the carpenter's family. Each new spring had found Jesus an inch or more taller. His boyish voice had become deep like a man's and his face was bearded. Some of his brothers and sisters had married and had children of their own.

Slowly, year by year, Jesus' father had grown more feeble until he was no longer able to work in the shop. All day long he would sit on a stool in the courtyard, sometimes carving small figures in wood, sometimes talking or sleeping. Then came the morning when he fell asleep and could not be wakened. With his father's death, Jesus knew a great loneliness. Of all the sons, he had been the most intimate with his father. Who was there now to whom he could talk as freely? Strict as his father had been, Jesus had always felt a sureness in his love and respect.

Now Jesus was the manager of the shop. He it was who said the prayers before and after eating and who began to teach his brothers' children the customs of his people.

Every year since that first visit to Jerusalem, when he was twelve years old, Jesus had gone down to the city to attend at least one of the yearly festivals. Each time he entered that beautiful and stately temple, the less interested he became in the sacrificing of animals and in the bringing of offerings and the more eager he was to spend the hours with the teachers who explained the old books. Naturally, Jesus himself began to take more part in the discussions. The more he learned, the more questions he had to ask, and the stronger grew his purpose to become a teacher himself.

But Jesus had returned to his carpenter's shop in Nazareth each year, busying himself, as his father had done before him, with ox yokes and carts, with doors and tables. Occasionally someone would bring him news that a traveling teacher was spending a few days in Nazareth. Jesus would then leave his shop for as many

The more he learned, the more questions he had to ask

hours as he could, and go to the market place or to the synagogue to hear the man. In this way, by using every opportunity that came, Jesus grew wise regarding the sacred books of his people and he learned the teachings of the later rabbis.

Jesus had long since broken with the Young Patriots, but only after much wrestling with his own thoughts and after many heated arguments with the other boys. Although for a long time they were bitterly sarcastic about his decision, Jesus never quite lost their friendship and respect. Zebedee and Joash had joined the guerrillas. No one knew where they were then hiding. Zadok's family had moved to Tiberias, where there was more work for a weaver to do than in Nazareth. David was still caring for sheep on the hills above the town, just as his father had done before him.

If, by chance, one of the Young Patriots in hiding did come back to Nazareth for a day, he was sure to look up Jesus. And just as surely a heated discussion would again begin. Always, sooner or later, the same old questions would come up that the boys used to thrash over at their meetings. How soon would the Messiah come? How would they know him when he appeared? What should they do while they were waiting for his coming? What was the Kingdom of God for — was it just to set the Jewish people free from their Roman bondage? Would the Jews then be masters of the Romans? How would that help to bring real goodness among men?

As a young man, Jesus had grown in the favor of his neighbors. They saw that carpentry was not the whole of his life. It was a common thing for them to drop in at the shop, not to place an order but just to visit. In the evenings, friends would gather on the housetop and there they would often talk long into the night. Of course it was not the leaders of the House of Meeting who came nor the merchants from the other end of the town. Jesus was popular with people — weavers and potters, tailors and farmers — people who had never even had as good a chance as he to go to school. Some of those who came were foreigners — Greeks, Phoenicians and Arabs — who talked with foreign accents and who had never gone to the synagogue school. All these people had learned that it was safe to speak out their minds freely to Jesus.

The Sabbath afternoon was a favorite time for these neighborly conversations, and the top of the Nazareth hill was a favorite spot because of the breezes and the wonderful view. Jesus would sometimes take with him his own precious scroll of Isaiah and he would read to the others.

One day, a farmer burst out with this: "Yesterday the tax collector made me give him as my taxes one whole bushel out of my small crop of olives."

"That was nothing but robbery!" shouted the friend alongside. "The old traitor probably sold the bushel and kept half the money for himself."

"But now," continued the farmer, "I must still give my tax to the temple. That will be one out of every ten bottles of olive oil I make. Yes, one out of ten of everything I raise. If I do not pay these taxes, the priests in Jerusalem will warn the people who come to the market not to buy my products. They will tell them that some dreadful calamity will come if they buy of me. What am I to do? If I pay all these taxes my children must go hungry. If I do not pay the taxes, I cannot sell the rest of my crops."

A stonecutter had another complaint. He asked: "How can I afford to give up one of my goats and take it to the temple to be offered on the altar? I do not have enough milk as it is to feed my children. Won't God listen to my prayer for forgiveness unless I give up this goat as a burnt offering?"

Jesus himself also was puzzled over such matters. Sometimes he would sit quietly without saying a word. What things were most important for a good person to do? Which of these rules was it really necessary to follow in order to be pleasing to God? Jesus had begun to feel that there was something wrong about some of the teachings given by the rabbis. He had come to think very much as the prophet Micah had long before: "And what doth the Lord require of thee, but to do justly, and to love mercy, and to walk humbly with thy God?" Yes, those were the important things — justice, kindness and a humble spirit. How relieved everyone was to hear Jesus say this! But sometimes Jesus wished he could talk things over with a really great teacher. The scribes[1] in the synagogue thought him ignorant since he had never gone to school in Jerusalem. At times Jesus felt lonely with his thoughts.

Then something happened that caused Jesus to change the plans for his life. He met a great preacher, and this is how it came about.

A traveling merchant passing through the town stopped at the carpenter's shop to have a cart wheel repaired. The man had an exciting story to tell. Down in Judea near the banks of the Jordan he had heard a most extraordinary preacher.

"People by the hundreds are walking many miles to hear him. It's not at all pleasant there in that wilderness, with the sun beating down on those dry, rocky cliffs. But still the people come in crowds. The preacher looks almost as wild as the country he lives in, with his long, uncut hair and his short tunic of camel's skin. He's stern, too, and almost fierce sometimes. He reminds me of what Elijah must have been like."

"What is the man's name?" asked Jesus.

"They call him John the Baptizer."

"Does he live in that barren country all the time?" asked Jesus.

"Yes, he's one of a colony of hermits who believe in the simple life. They live on such foods as dried locusts and wild honey."

"Is John an old man?" asked Jesus. "Has he studied with the great teachers in Jerusalem?"

"John is a young man like yourself, Jesus. They say he was trained as a priest in the temple, but that he became discontented with so much sham in the ceremonies and with the money-making

[1]Another name for those who taught the Scriptures.

schemes of the high priests. So he left his home and his father's work and went to live with these hermits in the Judean wilderness."

"Tell me more," asked Jesus earnestly. "What does John preach? Is he trying to make more hermits?"

"A few join the colony in the wilderness. But John tells the people to go back to their own homes and live justly with their neighbors, not to rob the poor nor to hurt anyone. He says we should share what we have with those who have less."

"It would be good to hear a man talk plainly like that," said Jesus. "But why do you call John stern and almost fierce?"

"Because he warns the people that if they do not do justly a terrible day of punishment is coming for them. He says it doesn't matter who they are. He's afraid of no man. I tell you I never heard a man speak so powerfully. People change after being with John."

"And why do you call him the Baptizer?" asked Jesus.

"We call him the Baptizer," the stranger went on, "because he believes that being washed in water is a sign. Those hermits bathe themselves often — at least twice a day, morning and evening. To them bathing is not just for the body. It is a sign that the heart, too, is clean in God's sight. So John tells those to be baptized who have humbly asked God to forgive them and who are determined to live justly. He takes them down to a shallow place in the River Jordan and together they walk into the water. One by one he dips them under and when they rise from the water, John prays for them. It helps them to remember."

As the stranger was leaving the shop, Jesus thanked him for the good news he had brought. "Our people need a great prophet," said Jesus. "We are like lost sheep, fearful and troubled, calling for our shepherd to lead us back into the fold."

Later, when Jesus' mother called him for supper, he was singing lustily. A new hope had been born in him. Here at last was a teacher after his own heart. Jesus had his mind made up. He would leave his shop for a while and go down to the Judean wilderness to hear John the Baptizer for himself.

Not long after this, Jesus was there in the hot valley sitting on the rocks in the midst of a crowd listening to the hermit preacher.

And what a strange lot they were! Some wore flowing robes adorned with broad fringes and tassels. Others wore only ragged tunics reaching just to their knees. There were women, too, with necklaces of bright beads and coin decorations in their caps. Here and there were even a few tax collectors. Jesus knew them by the badges they wore. A couple of Roman soldiers in uniform sat a bit aloof from the crowd watching.

The preacher's voice sounded like blasts from a trumpet. "There is just one thing that is important. Repent! Turn from your evil ways! We shall never be a free people until we are a good people. The new kingdom for which we have all been waiting is near at hand. Without warning the great Deliverer will appear."

"Praise the Lord. Blessed be his name," shouted the listeners.

"Hold back your shouts of praise!" thundered the voice. "The day of the Messiah will not be a day of gladness, as you suppose. It will, rather, be a terrible day — the day of God's great anger. It will be a day when all those who do evil will be punished — yes, even destroyed. God's messenger will be like a farmer winnowing his wheat. Those who have lived justly will be like the good grains of wheat and those who have lived unjustly will be like the chaff which the wind blows away and which later is burned."

"Right! Right!" shouted the crowd. "God will have his revenge on our enemies."

"We are like trees," the preacher went on. "Some of us bear good fruit and some of us bear no fruit of any value at all. The Messiah will be like a farmer who comes to his orchard with his ax. Only the good trees will he allow to live in his orchard. The useless trees he will cut down and burn. The Almighty has no favorites. To him there are but two kinds of people — the good and the bad."

"All Jews are safe," shouted a scribe. "The Kingdom is for us, the children of Abraham. The evil-doers are our Roman enemies and all that have oppressed us. They are the ones to repent."

"I tell you," shouted John. "God is able of these stones to raise up children for Abraham. Whether we are Jews or foreigners matters not in the sight of God. What matters is whether we do those things that are right. Repent, therefore, I say, else God's anger will fall upon you."

At this several men arose and left. But most of the crowd stayed on. Some began to cry out anxiously, "What must we do to escape God's punishment?"

"He that has two coats, let him give one of them to a person who has no coat at all. And he that has more food than he needs, let him give half to someone else who has not what he needs."

"This is a true man of God!" thought Jesus. "How simple his teachings and yet how hard to do! And how different from saying prayers and bringing money to the temple!"

Then a tax collector mustered up courage to speak, "And what must a tax collector do? I suppose it is hopeless for us to escape God's anger."

"Not at all," answered John. "Your work is honorable if you make it so. In gathering taxes take no more than is due you."

Even a soldier braved the question, "And what can I do?"

"Never accuse anyone falsely. Never take a person's belongings away from him by force. Be content with your wages."

"What a man this John is!" thought Jesus. Never before had he heard a preacher tell tax collectors and Roman soldiers that they could share in the goodness of the new world that was coming. He watched the puzzled faces about him. John was holding out an opportunity to everyone — whether Jew or foreigner. After all, why not? Were not all men children of God?

As Jesus listened and watched, he wondered: "Should I, too, become a follower of this John?"

5 The Great Decision

JESUS lingered beside the Jordan River day after day, watching the crowds coming and going. He was fascinated to see how seriously they took everything the hermit preacher was saying. Under his stormy scoldings, some would weep or watch his stern face with frightened eyes. Others would nod their heads vigorously, or cheer his promises that the wicked would be destroyed. They all believed that John was a man sent from God. He was speaking the truth; at any cost, they would do whatever he told them to do.

Each evening the preacher would ask all those who had newly repented of their wrong-doings to come down into the river with him and be baptized as a sign of their changed purpose. Then a number of men and women would walk down into the shallow edge of the river. Standing with bowed heads, they would beg God to be merciful to them; then the preacher would lead them one by one into the deeper water; after praying for God's blessing he would dip them under. Over and over Jesus watched the people's faces as they came up out of the water. There was a glad, strong look in their eyes. He could see that they really meant to do as they had promised.

Jesus himself was also stirred as he had never been stirred by any teacher before. Had he not been saying some of these very things up in Nazareth when his friends had asked him questions? But John could say them with such power. These people were starting afresh on a new way of living. How thrilling it would be to see people change as a result of one's teaching!

This was real goodness John was talking about. It was not

merely bringing offerings to the temple, or saying prayers, or fasting twice a week. Such goodness as John was preaching was the one thing that really mattered. And if everyone would do what John was preaching, what a great change there would be everywhere! Jesus was all for this new way of life. No one was more convinced than he that John was speaking the truth. None was more ambitious than Jesus to find out what was right in the sight of God and to do it.

The enthusiasm of the crowds was contagious. Jesus was feeling as they felt. He, too, yearned to have his heart made clean of all false pride. He, too, wanted to feel that God had accepted him. He could then be strong for anything no matter how hard. Presently, Jesus also stepped forward into the river. John prayed for him, too, and he was dipped into the flowing water.

But Jesus had not realized how solemn the moment would be when he stood beside John in the water, and they prayed together. He forgot all about the water and the crowds and even about John. Jesus felt for the moment almost as though he were in heaven itself and standing before God. It seemed as if he were hearing a voice saying, "You are a loved son. I am pleased with you." At that moment Jesus knew that he, too, must prepare to be a teacher.

As he stepped out of the water and up the bank, he felt a longing to be alone. So he walked away from the crowds, and wandered up the rocky hillside. Jesus felt he had important things to straighten out in his own mind. How far he would go into this lonely country and how long he would stay he had no idea. He gave no thought to what he would eat or where he would sleep, or to the danger from the wild animals of the wilderness. He knew that thoughts were shaping in his mind, but they were not yet clear. There was something more he must decide. He would not hurry. He felt it was important to be sure of his own thoughts.

For days, Jesus wandered alone over the stony fields. Again and again he went over in his mind all the things he could remember in the Scriptures about the Kingdom of God. What kind of kingdom? How would it come? The changes John was asking for take place in people's lives quietly and unseen.

But John had talked also about something else. He said this other thing would come suddenly and soon. It was something that people could see. A Messiah would appear coming down from heaven. He would destroy the wicked with fire, and would gather the righteous in a place by themselves where they could live justly together. John was calling people to repent quickly so that they would not be destroyed when this terrible Day of the Lord came. Was this God's way of ridding the world of evil — by killing all the bad people? Jesus did not think so.

*At that moment Jesus knew that he, **too**, must prepare to be a teacher*

Which kind of kingdom, then, did Jesus believe in? Which would he work for? Would he preach the same message John was preaching? Or did he have something different to say? Jesus remembered the time when he and his father had sat together beside the ploughed field. As he thought about that day, the words from Isaiah came into his mind again:

And as the garden causeth the things that are sown in it to
  spring forth;
So the Lord God will cause righteousness and praise to
  spring forth before all the nations.

Yes, this was something different from John's preaching. The Kingdom of God would grow quietly and slowly, as seeds grow. It was something hidden in men's hearts in the same way seeds are hidden in the ground. The Kingdom of God was already growing in the hearts of many good people. Jesus was sure of this.

Yet at other times — perhaps it was when he was hungry or tired or discouraged — he would think that maybe God would have to do something miraculous and spectacular to make goodness grow. Men were hard hearted and proud. Perhaps they had to be frightened into goodness after all. Was John right, then?

So for days Jesus' thoughts went back and forth as he wandered restlessly over the rocky hills. He did not care to eat. His sleep was troubled with strange dreams. Finally, three dreams of a special kind came to him. They were so real he could not forget them.

In the first dream, Jesus saw himself sitting before a group of people and teaching them, when the Devil came up to him and whispered, "You think you are a Man of God. If you really are such a person, God will do a miracle for you to prove it if you ask him. How impressed your listeners would be if suddenly you told the stones at your feet to turn into bread and they instantly changed — just like that. Think of all the hungry people you could feed! And how they would praise you! They would know then that you were a true Man of God and they would believe anything you told them."

"No!" Jesus heard himself say to the Devil in his dream. "The Scriptures say that food for our bodies is not the only thing that people should live by. Food for our spirits — the truth from God — is more important. That is the kind of food I shall give to people."

The Devil could find no answer, and Jesus awoke.

In the second dream, Jesus thought he was back in the great temple in Jerusalem and that the Devil came and took him up to the highest pinnacle of that great building.

"You believe yourself to be a Man of God, don't you?" said the Devil. "Think, then, how impressed the people below in the city would be if you let yourself fall gently down from here right among them. It would seem to them that you had really come down from heaven. They would hail you as the Messiah, and God would let nothing hurt you; the Scriptures promise that."

"No!" said Jesus again. The thought seemed foolish to him. "Such a miracle would be unworthy of God. I cannot ask it of him."

Again the Devil could find no answer, and Jesus awoke.

In the third dream, the Devil came to Jesus once more and led him up to the top of a very high mountain such as Jesus had never climbed before. From this great height he could see for miles in all directions. He felt as though he were looking out on all the kingdoms of the world.

"Think of the glory of the one who shall be king above all other kings, ruling all the kingdoms of the earth. That's what the prophets have promised for the Messiah. Why couldn't you be he?"

Then Jesus turned to the Devil and said, "Get behind me where I can't see you or hear you speak. If I should strive for such a Kingdom it would be like falling down and worshiping you, the Prince of all Evil. No, I say! The commandment of God is 'Thou shalt worship the Lord thy God and him only shalt thou serve.' "

When Jesus awoke from this third dream, he believed that something deep within him had spoken. He began to feel at peace with himself. At last he knew the kind of Kingdom he would preach about. He knew now that he could not teach in John's way or speak John's ideas. He must speak his own thoughts, and these had grown clearer during these days alone with himself and God. He had no more dreams of the Devil.

But would the people listen to him? He would predict no startling doom. He would not be a hermit. He would go quietly from town to town teaching the truth as he saw it. He would never ask God to prove the truth of his teaching by making a miracle. He would trust people, and he would trust the truth to make them free. All this seemed very simple and without glamour. Yet what he wanted to teach was important. It would make a difference if people did believe him. It seemed as important as his own life. It seemed as true as God himself.

As Jesus walked back toward the river, he came at last to the place where John and the crowds had been, and where he himself had been baptized. Here to his surprise he found only a tent and a few hermits sitting on the rocks. Seeing that Jesus was tired and hungry, the men took pity on him and shared their simple meal of wild honey and locusts.

"But where is the Preacher?" asked Jesus.

"Have you not heard?" answered the leader. "Alas! We are filled with weeping. A few days ago, Herod sent his spies here to watch our Master. Herod had heard he was stirring up the people to think that a new kingdom was coming. The spies decided John was a dangerous rebel. So suddenly one day, even while he was preaching, they seized him and led him off to Herod's fortress in the wilderness beyond the Dead Sea. Since he is kept in stocks in the open court during a part of each day, some of us go to see him frequently and take him food. We try to encourage him to think he will be freed, but we tremble for his life."

Like a heavy, black cloud that blots out the daylight this unexpected news darkened Jesus' spirits. Of all the men whom he had ever known, John the Baptizer seemed the greatest. Jesus had been hoping to talk things over with John again. He had looked to John to rouse more and more people to repent and to seek righteousness. And now the voice of the great preacher was hushed. It was as if he were already dead. How could so much happen in so short a while? The suddenness of it all startled him. Jesus was aware as never before that he was living in a dangerous time for those who would speak new thoughts.

For a while he could say nothing to his companions. His words trembled at the door of his mouth. He tried to tell the hermits how greatly he respected their leader and how much he had hoped from him. He then thanked them for their hospitality and went on his way.

As the glow of the setting sun reddened the cliffs above the river, Jesus was climbing with strong steps up the steep pathway towards the highlands above. He was going back to his home and to his friends in Nazareth. Knowledge of John's arrest had merely strengthened his purpose to prepare to be a teacher. From now on he was going to be more than just a carpenter. A voice within him seemed to say, "You have a light. Do not hide it under a bushel, but put it on a stand so that those who pass by may see the way."

When at last darkness hid the path from his eyes, he lay down upon the ground to sleep. A feeling of loneliness came over him then, like the blackness of the night. Who was there now with whom he could talk things over? The noble John was out of reach. His own father was no more. His mother and brothers would not understand. Finally, a peace came gently upon him, like the shining of the moon in the sky. He was no longer alone, for God seemed nearer to him even than his own hands and feet.

6 Adventuring Forth Alone

BACK in Nazareth once more with his family, Jesus talked a great deal about the preacher he had heard. He described how he had seen rich and poor, even tax collectors and soldiers, praying for forgiveness and being baptized in the Jordan River. He told also of how he himself had been baptized and of the unforgettable experiences he had had afterwards alone in the wilderness. For many years Jesus had wanted to be a teacher. Now he was sure it was the thing to do. He must give up carpentry. He must leave his home. His brothers would have to take over the shop and their mother's care. God had spoken to his soul.

"You have lost your mind!" said his brother Joseph, scornfully.

"Who are you to presume to know enough to teach others?" shouted Judas.

"You have a responsibility to the family," pleaded Simon. "Without you, how can we feed all the mouths to be fed?"

"There are four of you," said Jesus. "You are all grown men. I will give up my claim to our home and shop and field."

"But how can you keep yourself alive?" asked James.

"I am not anxious about that," said Jesus. "I shall live a day at a time." He held out a bunch of field lilies he had gathered on the way home. "Look at these lilies! How do they grow? They do not toil, neither do they spin, yet even King Solomon in all his glory was never so beautifully arrayed as one of these. Are we not more valuable than flowers? You are always anxious, saying: What shall we eat? What shall we drink? I tell you life is more than food. We are more important than our clothes."

But James was anxious. "Are you going to the Judean wilderness to live as a hermit?" he asked.

"No, James. I want to live among people, to talk with them in their homes and in their market places and beside the village wells. Sometimes I hope I may speak in their synagogues."

All this talk annoyed Joseph and Simon. Judas walked off as if he did not care. James alone had a word of encouragement. Jesus' mother could only weep. She had visions of her son being put in prison as John had been. She never expected to see him again if he left home. She could not be comforted.

But Jesus remained sure of the rightness of his decision. If he gave himself to the one thing that was important to him, everything else he needed would be supplied somehow. He was not anxious.

These unexpected plans of the young carpenter's were gossiped about all over the town. Some of the townsfolk were for and some were against his new adventure. The ruler of the synagogue was inclined to be critical, but he asked Jesus to speak the next morning at the Sabbath service. "I shall give you a chance to explain yourself," he said.

The people who gathered at the House of Meeting were full of curiosity. Jesus felt the seriousness of the hour, yet his hopes were high. He would speak out bravely as John had done.

After the prayers and the chants and the first reading from the scroll of the Law, the attendant brought from the sacred ark a scroll of Isaiah and gave it to Jesus. Standing behind the pulpit, Jesus opened the scroll at the place where Isaiah had told how he had felt when the conviction came to him that he should be a preacher to his people. When Jesus had read a short portion, he rolled up the scroll and gave it back to the attendant and sat down. The eyes of all were fastened on him, as he began to speak.

"What happened to Isaiah has now happened to me. I, too, believe God has spoken to my soul. He has bidden me to preach the good news I have come to believe is the truth. It will gladden the poor and the discouraged. We are enslaved not only to the Roman power, but by false teachings as well. We are prisoners bound to our ceremonies and to our prayers which must be said word for word. The taxes demanded by our high priests and the sacrifices required of us for the temple are like heavy burdens that make us weary and fainthearted. We are continually afraid of the anger of God and of his punishments if we do not meet all these demands. I want our people to believe that God is more ready to give us good things than a father is to give good things to his child."

For some time Jesus talked in this outspoken manner.

When he had finished and the service was ended, the people were disturbed. Some of the thoughts Jesus had spoken were beautiful beyond anything they had ever heard. Others of his thoughts cut like a sword.

"Is not this the carpenter's son? Where did he get these new ideas? Who is he to think he is better than our rabbis?"

The rulers of the synagogue were positively angry. This young man would destroy their religion. They would have nothing more to do with him. Two of his old teachers took hold of Jesus, one on each side, and led him out of the synagogue. A crowd followed them through the streets and up the road that led toward the hill above the city.

"Never let us see your face in our synagogue again!" they said. And they pushed him from them. They wished in their hearts they could push him over the cliff. That would be a quick end to his boldness. But they did not dare. Instead they left him and turned back toward the town, with the crowd at their heels.

Jesus disappeared down the road in the opposite direction. Without food or water, with no chance to say good-by to his mother or brothers or sisters, he wandered off alone, perhaps never to return.

He found a path over a hill. He wanted to keep away from any town for a while. He needed time to collect his thoughts. He wanted to pray where none but God would see. Perhaps he had been too outspoken. Why should he have thought that his neighbors would understand? He would have to learn to be more patient, more friendly. He would have to begin all over again in a town where nobody knew him.

The following morning he had a plan. He would go to Capernaum at the north end of the Lake of Galilee. He thought he would like fishermen. He could fish with them and so they would be friends.

By mid-afternoon he reached the hillside above the town of Capernaum. As he began climbing down to the harbor on the edge of a little bay in the lake, every now and then he stopped just to

48

He wandered off alone,
perhaps never to return

look out on the wondrous blue water spread out below, resting as it were in the gentle arms of the green hills all around.

He was soon stepping around between the fish nets spread out on the grass. Hundreds of smelly fish, laid out on beds of palm leaves, had been drying all day in the sun. Shortly he was down in the midst of the noisy crowd on the wharf. Men were carrying bags of grain and baskets of fruits and vegetables, and loading them into boats to be rowed across the lake and sold. In and out went the tax collectors gathering their heavy fees in spite of the heated protests of the owners; Roman soldiers stood guard here and there to be ready to settle any quarrels that might go beyond words.

Capernaum was a fisherman's town and Jesus liked people who worked. He was not particular whether they were rich or poor.

49

Everybody was interesting to Jesus. So he soon made friends. Even the very first evening, a husky, outspoken fisherman called Peter invited Jesus to his home for the night. It was a pleasant home with a court and a garden, and Peter lived there alone with his mother-in-law and his little boy, Mark. Since Peter's wife had died but a short while before, he was especially glad for company. The next morning after prayers and the morning meal, the mother-in-law knew she was going to like Jesus. "You must stay right here in our house all the time you are in Capernaum," she said as he was leaving to go to the wharf. "We have an extra room on the roof; it shall be yours as long as you care to have it. We feel honored to have a teacher in our home. You can see for yourself how happily Mark follows you around. Peter is a good fisherman; he provides well for our comfort, but you feed something more than our bodies." Jesus was pleased with that.

Soon he began to feel quite at home in Peter's house, and he was happy in knowing that at last he was teaching as he had been wishing he could do ever since he was a boy. It was not long before other people discovered that there was in the town a man who had most interesting things to say.

After the morning's haul of fish had been brought in and salted and spread out to dry, and after the women had mended the fish nets and laid them out on the grass, and the fishermen had eaten, everyone felt at leisure. Then Jesus would come down to the lake-side and make friends with the people. He would ask them questions and tell them stories. Strangely enough, they soon began telling him things they had never dared to tell anyone else before.

Sometimes he would go down to the lakeside after supper in the cool of the evening when all was quiet. The fishermen would bring the women and older boys along with them. Then they would start Jesus talking, and the people would all sit around on the grass and rocks. One evening the crowd became so large and the people pressed so close about Jesus that some could not see the teacher.

So Peter rowed one of his boats up along the shore and asked Jesus to stand up in the boat and talk from there where all could see and hear.

"What a beautiful picture Jesus makes as he stands there with the blue of the lake just behind him," said one of the women.

But not everyone in the crowd noticed the loveliness of the scene, for they were worried over the day's happenings.

"It's no longer safe to travel alone anywhere," said an excited fisherman who evidently had a story to tell. "Robbers are lurking on every highway."

"What's happened?" asked his companion, who had passed the day peacefully and happily.

"Haven't you heard what they did to James today?" asked the fisherman in surprise. "He was pulling his cartload of fish along the road to Nain where he counted on selling them, when a man, stepping out from a side path, joined him and began chatting in a seemingly friendly manner. Now James, because the sun was hot, had taken off his outer cloak and, tying it into a bundle, he had hung it on his cart.

"The stranger saw the cloak and said, 'I need that cloak of yours for one of our guerrilla band.' And without asking James for his leave, the stranger suddenly grabbed the cloak and tried to pull it off the cart.

" 'But you can't have that cloak!' said James stubbornly. 'It's mine!'

" 'I have orders to bring ten cloaks into our hiding place. You have another cloak at home; you can spare this to a man who's fighting for your country.'

"James grew hot with anger. He tried to snatch the cloak away from the stranger. 'You have no right to take this from me. You're a thief.'

"Then the man struck James on the cheek and James struck back, and the man struck James again on the other cheek. In a moment, the cloak was stripped off, the cart upset, the fish thrown all around in the dust, and James left lying helpless on the ground, his face bleeding."

"Such violence as this would end if the Romans would leave us alone," said one man in the crowd.

"But that's no excuse for robbing your own countrymen," shouted back another.

"It's the Romans who are keeping us poor. We should kill every Roman soldier in the land!" a man in the back of the crowd called bitterly. The people on the grass began to squirm uneasily. Perhaps a Roman was even then spying on them.

Jesus could almost feel their bitterness like a rush of wind in his face as he stood listening from the boat. He, too, had once felt much the same way. It was natural to become angry when unjustly treated and to want to rise up to harm one's enemy; but at last, for himself, Jesus had found a way to take cruelty. But could he explain his thoughts? At least he would try. So he began.

"You know well the old commandment, 'Thou shalt not kill,' and you have been told that he who murders another will be judged by God as a wicked person and will be punished for his crime." Jesus' voice was calm but decisive. "But I say to you, when one person becomes angry with another, the crime has already begun. It is the angry wish to hurt or destroy another that is wrong in the sight of God. Whoever calls another person by a mean name such as 'you fool,' has already killed something in the person to whom he has spoken. Let us not think that only those who kill the body are bad people. There is badness in anyone who becomes angry with another." The listening crowd was very quiet. Jesus went on.

"You have been told that the old law says, if two people get into a quarrel and one hurts the other, the one who is hurt shall demand that the one who has hurt him must suffer in exactly the same way. If he has made a man blind in one eye, he must have one of his own eyes put out. If he has struck out a tooth or lamed a hand or foot, he must have a tooth of his own knocked out or his own hand or foot lamed.

"But I say to you, resist not him that is evil. Do not fight back. If a man strikes you on one cheek, turn to him the other cheek and let him hit that, too. And if a man takes away your outside cloak, let him have your inside coat also. If a man compels you to walk a mile with him and makes you carry his load, walk two miles instead."

"Who gave you the right to change the Law of Moses?" shouted one of the leaders from the House of Meeting.

"Impossible! Impossible!" said the man who had told the story about James and the robber. "You surely do not mean that we should treat our enemies like that. If we did, every single one of us would soon be dead."

"You have heard it said," Jesus continued, " 'Love your neighbors and hate your enemies.' But I say to you, love your enemies, do good to them that hate you. Bless them that curse you, and pray for them that shamefully use you.

"If you love them that love you, what thanks do you deserve for that? Everyone can love those that love him. And if you do good only to those who do good to you in return, what thanks do you deserve? Everyone can do that. I say to you, love your enemies as well as your friends."

Then Jesus paused and looked up at the sky. The glow from the setting sun made the soft clouds glorious in their colors. He began to tell his thoughts.

"Here we all are enjoying this gorgeous sunset together. God is not sending this beauty to us alone; it is spread out before our enemies as well. God makes the sun shine on the evil as well as on the good. He also sends his rain on those who are unjust as well as on those who are just. Let us be like God so that we may be worthy to be called sons of the Father of all people. Let us not exclude anyone when we send out our good feelings."

In amazement, these fishermen and women had listened. Some of the teachers grew angry at Jesus' words. "Who is this man to put his words above the words of the Holy Book?" they cried. "He is destroying our Law!"

"Not at all," came back the answer. "He is making the Law have more sense. If only we could do it, who can say what great things might come about? I'd like to learn how to be the way he says."

"I like the way he talks out his own ideas. Most teachers stick to what people of long ago have said, and are afraid to think for themselves."

"Give me time. I must think more about these new ideas."

So the crowd scattered, each man and woman thinking his own thoughts, and each one saying to the other, "We never heard anything like this before."

7 Sick and Unforgiven

BEFORE long Jesus had many friends in the town of Capernaum. It was strange what an effect he had on people. Old men and old women when they listened to him began to feel younger. Others who had been sick were going back to their daily work again, feeling made over like new. There were those also who had got into the habit of feeling afraid of many things; they expected, for example, that some bad spirit might slip into their homes almost any day to make one of their children sick. These timid folk began to look more carefree as if they were no longer bothered by such thoughts.

All over the town were people who kept watch on Jesus to make sure they would not miss hearing him whenever he let the people gather around him. Rich and poor, teachers who knew the best learning of the schools and people who could not even read, invited Jesus to their homes for a meal. They said they felt greatly honored to have such a man come under their roofs.

But it was in Peter's home that Jesus most often stayed. Peter had a comfortable space on the roof of his house and there was a pleasant courtyard where friends could gather in the evenings. Then, too, as Peter's family was small Jesus could find quiet there, and Peter's mother-in-law could never do enough for him.

Jesus also found that Peter was a great help to him in getting acquainted with the townspeople, for he had lived in Capernaum all his life. He seemed to know everybody. Jesus would often sit in the quiet courtyard in the evening and Peter would tell him of one after another of his neighbors. He knew their stories from the time they were babies in arms.

One evening as the two sat together on the roof top, Peter was telling of the different men whom Jesus had seen during the day — the hunchback, the captain of the Roman squadron, the rich old tax collector who lived in the big house on the hill, and so on. Then Peter came to the story of Nathan.

"Nathan is a good man if ever there was one," said Peter. "He was the best student of the Holy Book that Capernaum has ever had. He used to spend months at a time in Jerusalem sitting at the the feet of the teachers in the temple. He could give you perfectly any law you wanted to know about anything under the sun."

"And did Nathan keep the laws himself in his own everyday living?" asked Jesus.

"No one ever tried harder than Nathan to be good," said Peter. "Nathan used to pray faithfully three times a day and more. He would go two whole days a week without food in order to have more time to spend in prayer. Regularly once a year, he spent his hard-earned money for a perfect one-year-old goat and had it sacrificed in the temple. He would say, 'I have probably done something wrong without knowing it. I want to be sure God has forgiven me.' Nathan was very careful also to save one-tenth of all his earnings to give to the temple. He would even take out a tenth part of every kind of vegetable in his garden, and give it to the House of Meeting. And what made Nathan such a favorite in the town was that he always knew when anyone was sick or without enough food and he would take them baskets of bread and fruit."

"Nathan was surely a good man," said Jesus. "Many can teach the laws of God, but few are those who live by the laws themselves."

"But Nathan is not like that any more," said Peter solemnly. "He's a sick man now who doesn't care about anything. The change in him took place just a year ago in Jerusalem. He was walking down the Street of the Gardeners. The farmers from the country and the farmers from around Jerusalem were displaying their vegetables in booths along the street. He noticed that the country farmers were selling their produce cheaper than the Jerusalem farmers were selling theirs, and, of course, the Jerusalem farmers did not like this.

"Then Nathan saw something that put bitterness into his heart. Two priests walked down the street. Nathan heard them saying to the shoppers they passed, 'Do not buy vegetables from the country farmers. Their food is not clean. Before coming to the market they did not take a tenth part out of their crops to give to the temple. They do not obey the law. God will punish you with some kind of trouble if you eat their vegetables.' Nathan could scarecely believe the words his ears heard.

" 'So these are the priests who in their white robes offer our sacrifices for us in the temple!' thought Nathan. 'The next day they rob these poor farmers of their living in the name of God! How do these priests know whether these farmers have given their tenth or not? And are the Jerusalem farmers any better? These priests are not caring about real goodness. They are thinking only of how to keep the gifts and money coming into the temple treasury because they know that in the end most of this money becomes theirs. The poor are being robbed so that the high priest and his relatives may live in palaces!'

"Thoughts such as these began to burn in Nathan's mind. He could not bear to go into the temple again to worship. He would not bring gifts for these pretenders (as he called the priests) to offer and then to feast upon. So, with a heart full of trouble, Nathan wandered in and out of the streets of Jerusalem, until at last he found lodging in a fisherman's inn. There he became acquainted with a band of men who were on fire with a strange idea. They were robbers, but they thought themselves *good* robbers. Each night some of their number would raid some luxurious home in order to get back at least a little of the riches that had been stolen from the poor. Whatever these men pilfered from the rich, they would take great pleasure in giving away to their poor neighbors who were not even having enough to eat. It was strange how Nathan began to like these robbers. He was even persuaded to join them in one of their nightly raids.

"But Nathan was too good a man to be happy very long as a robber. When finally he awoke, as it were, from his bad dream, he was filled with shame. He felt he had knowingly done a great wrong. He had become a thief! God could never, never forgive him!

"Then Nathan's heart began to dry up. He left the robbers and returned to Capernaum, but he could not bear to walk the streets of his home town. He did not care to meet his old friends. For a long time, he could not even tell his wife what had happened to him. He took to his bed. He had no appetite for eating."

"Does Nathan think that God is still punishing him?" asked Jesus.

"Yes, he thinks that God has made him sick and that he must bear the punishment. I tell you, Jesus, I worry about Nathan every time I think about him. He was such a good man."

"Does he really seem sick to you?" asked Jesus.

"Yes, he is so weak and thin now, he can't even lift his hand to feed himself."

"I must go to see him," said Jesus. "It is a pity that so good a man should think God can understand so little. If Nathan's own child should ask bread of him, Nathan would not give the child a stone. Or if he ask for a fish, Nathan would not give a snake, or if the child asked for an egg, Nathan would not give his son a scorpion. If, then, Nathan, being a sinful father, knows how to give good things to his child, how much more shall our Father in heaven give a good thing like forgiveness when it is asked for?"

"Oh, how I wish Nathan could hear you talk," cried Peter. "His friends and his wife have been begging him to let them bring him to you, but over and over he has refused."

All the while as Peter had been telling this story of Nathan, the sound of voices in the courtyard below had been growing louder until it was so great that Jesus and Peter could scarcely hear each other speak.

"Perhaps you will take me tomorrow to see Nathan," said Jesus as they rose and looked over the wall to see what was happening. To their surprise, they saw the courtyard packed with excited men and women from all over the town — fishermen and their wives, farmers, teachers and strangers from the towns across the lake.

"Rabbi, Jesus," they shouted when they saw his face above the wall. "Come down and talk to us."

So Jesus and Peter went down the stairs to the little covered balcony that overlooked the courtyard. At once, the talkative crowd became still as the waters of the lake on a quiet summer's evening.

Just how long Jesus talked and just what he said, no one seems to have remembered, for presently a surprising thing happened that made them forget everything else.

Four men, carrying a fifth man stretched out on a sleeping mat, appeared on the roof above. They had been unable to make their way through the court because of the great crowd, so they had climbed to the roof of the adjoining house and walked across to the roof of Peter's house. Jesus and Peter could not see what had been happening, but from the looks on the faces of the crowd they knew something unusual was going on. So Jesus stopped speaking for the time, and waited. Presently to his surprise, a hole was made in the roof above his head. The men were pulling out the

*The sad look of discouragement
began slowly to fade out of his face*

leaves and sticks and hard cakes of mud until there was a large open space. Then the sick man on his mattress was carefully let down through the hole in the roof and laid at Jesus' feet. What a look of surprise came over Peter's face when he saw who the man was! "It is Nathan!" he whispered excitedly. "God be thanked!"

Jesus felt tears come to his eyes as he looked down on the pale, sad face. He stood for a while without saying a word. He was thinking to himself. "How these men must love Nathan! How sure they must be that I can help him! God cannot be angry with such an honest, good man. His sickness cannot be a punishment from God. His sickness is a pitiful mistake. It is all because his heart is discouraged. Will the man believe me if I tell him his sins are forgiven? It will cure him if only he will believe it."

Jesus decided to speak to the man firmly. "Nathan!" came the bold words. "God knows the goodness of your heart. He understands everything. Your sins are all forgiven!"

Nathan opened his eyes and looked up at Jesus with a faint smile. Jesus repeated his words. "Nathan, your sins are all forgiven." The sad look of discouragement began slowly to fade out of his face. Somehow Nathan could not help but believe Jesus, although he didn't know why. It was certainly more than the sure ·tone of his voice.

But a mumbling of angry voices rose from the crowd in the courtyard below. Jesus could not distinguish the words they were saying to one another, but he felt what they were thinking. Stepping nearer the wall, he looked down on the troubled crowd, and lifted his voice so that all could hear.

"You are wondering how I dare to speak for God. You are saying to yourselves, 'Who can forgive sins but God alone?' It is easy, in this case, to say 'Your sins are forgiven!' You know your good neighbor. You know how deeply he regrets his great mistake. It is right for us to assure such a man that he is forgiven."

Then turning again to the weak and helpless man on his mat,

Jesus said, "Nathan, stand up and walk! You need be sick no
longer. Pick up your bed and go home."

Then slowly, with a great effort, the man tried to lift his head.
His weakness could not leave him in a moment, but his courage
was coming back. His friends helped him gently to his feet, and
then later they carried him down the stairs. In the courtyard
Nathan put his feet on the ground. He took a step and then another. Two friends supported him.

The people made way for them and followed after, out the
gate in the wall. They were too deeply moved to have many words.
Some shook their heads solemnly and said, "We have seen strange
things today."

8 *More About Forgiving*

NEWS of the change that had come over Nathan spread from
house to house till the whole town knew the story. Indeed, the
fame of the young preacher from Nazareth was being carried to
other towns along the shore of the Galilean lake. Fishermen were
finding excuses for guiding their sailboats into the wharf at Capernaum in the hope of catching sight of this unusual person of whom
they were hearing. Crowds began to gather whenever the word
was whispered that Jesus had been seen on the streets or was sitting on the beach beside the lake.

Nathan was a popular citizen of Capernaum and an honor to
the society of Pharisees to which he belonged. To see him walking
the streets once more chatting in his old friendly way was some-

thing to celebrate. When his neighbors saw him again at his pot
ter's wheel, they found excuses to buy his handiwork. There was
beauty in the forms of the bowls and pitchers he molded. The
Tyrian blue he used in painting them made his pottery even more
distinctive. And when passers-by found Nathan in his garden in the
cool of the day pulling weeds and hoeing the earth, then they were
sure their friend was really well.

"I never feel so free with the other Pharisees in town as I do
with Nathan," said one of his neighbors. "No doubt he knows as
much as any of them, but he never sets himself off as better than
the rest of us, for all that."

The people knew Jesus had been right in telling Nathan his sins
were forgiven. They had never been able to find out what the
wicked thing was that he had done, but they were sure it had been
a mistake. They all knew that if they could have opened up
Nathan's heart as a book can be opened, and could have looked
inside, they would have found him to be all right.

But some of the other Pharisees, who had studied the laws
written in the books, were accusing Jesus of trying to play the part
of God. How could Jesus know whether the man's sins were forgiven? What right had he to do what only God could do? God
kept his own secret record in heaven of every man's deeds. The
good ones were listed in one column and the bad ones in another.
If a person did more wrong deeds than good ones, he would have to
make up in some way for his evil deeds. He would have to go
without food and pray long prayers, and bring animals to the temple in Jerusalem to be sacrificed and make gifts of money to the
synagogue and give more gifts to the poor, and so on and on.
When the good deeds more than balanced the evil deeds, the man
would be forgiven, but not until then. How could Jesus know
whether or not Nathan's record was balanced again? Nathan
hadn't gone to the temple for over a year, and he had even stopped
attending worship in the synagogue.

So the learned men talked, and the people who could not read the books of the Law for themselves were disturbed. "Won't you come to the synagogue on the Sabbath day and talk more about this matter of forgiving?" asked one of the fishermen of Jesus.

When the Sabbath came, the House of Meeting was filled to overflowing. Men crowded on the benches in front of the pulpit and the women squeezed into their little gallery behind the latticed railing where the men could not see their faces.

Jesus sat on the platform with three other men, the rulers of the town, and Nathan was back in his old place among them. Behind them all was a beautifully embroidered curtain — red and purple and blue — and behind the curtain was the holy ark or precious box in which the scrolls of Scripture were kept.

After the usual chanting of psalms, or songs of praise, and the saying of a number of long prayers, one of the men on the platform went behind the curtain and brought out a scroll and placed it on the pulpit. Unrolling the scroll to the place where he wished to read, Jesus began reading from the Fifty-first Psalm.

It was a prayer of David's, written after he had done a cruel thing to the poor owner of a vineyard near his palace. David was heartbroken because of the terrible wrong he had done and he was pleading with God for forgiveness:

Have mercy upon me, O Lord, according to thy loving-
    kindness; . . .
Thou desirest truth in the inward parts.
Thou delightest not in sacrifice; else would I give it:
Thou hast no pleasure in burnt offering.
The sacrifices of God are a broken spirit:
A broken and a contrite heart, O God, thou wilt not
    despise.

After the reading, the scroll was again rolled up and carried back safely to the ark behind the beautiful curtain, and Jesus began to speak.

"You have often heard it said that the only way to be sure of God's forgiveness is to take an offering to the temple; and in the Law of Moses it is clearly stated just what kind of offering must be brought for each kind of offence. But David in this psalm speaks of another way."

The men on the benches before Jesus leaned forward and raised their eyes with eagerness. Would he dare to speak against the holy temple and the Law?

Jesus went on. "Forgiveness is not something we can buy of God by bringing him gifts, or by sacrificing animals on the temple altar. What need has the Creator for the blood of sheep and of cattle? David even said that God takes no pleasure in burnt offerings. It is the change that takes place inside — in the feelings that have led us into the wrong — that brings forgiveness. The man who is heartbroken and repentant has already made the only sacrifice needed."

Many could not help but look at Nathan as Jesus was speaking. Nathan had lived for months with a broken heart.

Jesus had still more to say. "If, therefore, you are offering your gift at the altar, and there you remember that your brother has some cause for ill feeling toward you, leave your gift before the altar and go away to find your brother. First make peace with him, and then come back and offer your gift. . . . Blessed are the merciful, for they are the ones who will receive mercy in return.

"If we continue to despise those whom we have wronged, why should we ask God to forgive us? When we pray we should say, 'Forgive us our wrongdoings, just as we have forgiven those who have done us wrong.' For if you forgive others their wrongdoings toward you, then your Heavenly Father will also forgive you. But if you do not forgive others their wrongdoings, neither will your Heavenly Father forgive your wrongdoings."

Then Jesus told a story to show more plainly what he meant. "A certain king decided to settle accounts with his servants. When he had finished his reckoning, he called a man who owed him ten thousand talents.[1] Since the man had nothing with which to pay his debt, the king commanded that he be sold as a slave, and his wife and children also, and that everything he had be taken away from him until he could make the payment.

"The servant in his distress fell down on his knees and pleaded with the king, saying, 'Lord, have patience with me and I will pay you all.'

"Then the king had mercy on the servant and forgave him his debt, and freed him of his need to pay.

"But immediately the servant went out and found a servant of his who owed him one hundred pence.[2] He laid hold of the man, saying, 'Pay me what you owe me.'

"Then this servant fell down on his knees and humbly begged his master, saying 'Only have patience with me and I will pay you all.'

"But the man would not let his servant go. Instead he had him put into prison, until he should pay his debt.

"Now there were other servants of the king who learned what had happened and they went to the king and told him.

"The king called his servant back and said, 'You wicked servant! I forgave you all your debt to me because you begged so hard for me to do it. Should you not also have had mercy on the man who owed you money even as I had mercy on you?'

"Then the king was angry and had the man put under guard until he paid the whole debt.

"So shall our Heavenly Father do unto us, if we do not every one forgive our brothers from our hearts. This, then, is the surest way of knowing when God has forgiven us," said Jesus, "if we have no bitter feelings ourselves toward anyone. In this way we have power to forgive ourselves. God is always ready if we are."

[1] About $20,000,000 in American money.
[2] About $20 in American money.

While Jesus had been talking the three rulers stirred restlessly in their seats. Others, however, like Nathan, nodded their heads approvingly again and again while Jesus was speaking. Some of the people on the benches in front sat through his whole talk almost without moving, and with eyes opened wide with wonder. They had never heard anyone say such things before, and yet his words seemed too reasonable not to be true. It was strange how they began to feel less afraid of God, and yet somehow God seemed more glorious than ever before.

When once outside the door many began putting their feelings into words.

"A great prophet has arisen among us," said some. "We shall hear more from him."

"He made me think of all the mean things I have ever done to people," said another, "but I don't mind. I'm going to make amends where I can."

"Where did the man get his wisdom?" asked others. "He's only a carpenter from Nazareth. He has never been taught by the great rabbis."

"He doesn't need the teachers," called out another voice. "He has taught himself."

In the midst of the excitement, Peter and Andrew took Jesus away quietly from the crowd and down an out-of-the-way street to their home. When finally they were seated together around the low supper table, eating the simple meal Peter's mother-in-law had prepared, Peter put a question to Jesus.

"Rabbi," he said, "how often shall I let someone do wrong to me and still forgive him? Should I be ready to do it seven times?"

Jesus' reply was, "Yes, Peter, not only seven times, but until seventy times seven times."

And Peter was amazed at the patience Jesus expected of a man.

9 A New Venture Begins

NATHAN was not the only sick person in Capernaum who was made well simply by coming to know Jesus. Each one who had found his health improved told his friends and these would follow after Jesus expecting him to do as much for them.

This was not because Jesus encouraged people to think he was a doctor. He never set himself up as a healer of sickness, nor would he accept money for what he did. But his heart was too full of pity to send the sick off without some word of encouragement. He really would not do much. Perhaps he would merely lay his hand on the person's shoulder and say a friendly word. Strangely enough, some people, although by no means all the sick, came to have so much confidence in Jesus that the slightest sign from him to show he cared seemed to be all that was needed. They would go away almost forgetting their pains and before they knew it they were well. Jesus told them it was *they* who made themselves well, not he, but he could not always make them believe that.

No one knew how many sick people there were in Capernaum until a man like Jesus came to town. Some were sick simply because they were overworked or did not have enough to eat. Others were sick because they had let their bitter feelings against the Romans grow until their minds became mad with hatred. Those who became insane were driven out of their homes, and sometimes out of the town, and made to live by themselves in the hills. Almost everyone else was afraid of these people. Because Jesus was not frightened, he could do almost anything with them.

So the fame of Jesus as a healer of sickness spread beyond Caper-

Crowds would gather eve
before Jesus arrived

naum to other towns of Galilee, and people would come or would
be brought to him from many miles away. Whenever the rumor
spread that Jesus would be on a certain hillside or in someone's
house for dinner or down on the beach in the evening, crowds
would gather even before Jesus arrived, and they would wait for
him. People would run after him when they saw him on the street
in order to kiss the hem of his cloak. Or, if he sat under the shade
of the sycamore in the market place, they would come and kneel
at his feet and plead with him for help.

Fortunately, those who were not sick came as well as those who
were. People who ploughed the land, fishermen who rose before
daylight to fish, men who cut down the trees of the forests and dug
stones from the side of the hills and built the roads, poor women
who never had an extra penny beyond their simplest needs, tax

68

collectors who were not admitted to the synagogue — these were
they who made up the crowds of listeners. "Such ignorant people
don't know enough to know what is good or what is bad. Why
bother to teach them?" said the learned men who were correct in
their every deed. The poor and the untaught, however, always
heard Jesus gladly for to them what he said was "good news." He
made them feel that a better time was coming. The day of the
poor man was near.

They could not forget the way Jesus had said it one day:
Blessed are you that are poor: for yours is the kingdom of God.
Woe unto you that are rich: for you have received your comfort.
Blessed are you that hunger now: for you shall be filled.
Woe unto you that are full now: for you shall hunger.
Blessed are you that weep now: for you shall laugh.
Woe unto you that laugh now: for you shall mourn and weep.

When the people heard such words, gladness would shine in
their faces. Their eyes would twinkle, they would smile at one another, and nod their heads with approval.

But few among them understood how these things were to
come to pass. Nearly everyone seemed to expect it would all happen like a miracle. "Perhaps Jesus himself is the Messiah," they
thought. "He has such wonderful power over sick people, he might
have power as a leader of an army against the Romans." There
were those among them who belonged to the underground Society
of Patriots.[1] In secret, these men were already planning to rebel
as soon as they could muster enough fighters and find a strong
enough leader. "Perhaps Jesus can be persuaded," they thought.
"The people would all follow him if once he summoned them to
fight."

But Jesus was not interested in fighting, or in armies, or in kings
on their thrones. He was hoping for a goodness that could come
into people's living even though their country was still ruled by a
foreign power. His words could not conquer the armed battalions

[1]Usually referred to as Zealots.

of Rome. His pity could not throw down the stone walls of Herod's palaces, nor did he care to do these things. The trouble was that most people acted as though they lived on food alone, or that to be rich and able to buy many things was all that was needed to make one happy. No! Such things help only the body. What of the soul that is within the body? It was the soul that Jesus cared to make well and to free from falsehood and feelings of shame in the presence of God.

So Jesus was not well pleased by his own growing popularity. Too many came merely to be made well or to be assured that some day they would be rich and able to take vengeance on their enemies.

One night Jesus was very tired, having been followed by crowds the whole day long. He had spent so much time helping the sick that there had been almost none left to talk to those who were well. If this sort of thing kept up, he would have no time for teaching at all. That night as he lay trying to sleep, his mind was restless.

Long before daylight, he rose quietly. Folding his sleeping mat, he stepped softly down the stairs and out to the wooded hillside beyond the end of the street. He wanted to be alone, to think through his problem and to pray God for wisdom.

Later in the morning when Peter and his mother were up and about, they heard unusual noises in the street. Opening the door, Peter saw to his surprise that already a dozen sick people were sitting beside the road. When they saw Peter look out, they all began clamoring, "Where is Jesus? We're waiting for him."

Then Peter climbed the stairs to Jesus' room, calling, "Jesus, Jesus, there are people outside already waiting for you. What shall we do?" But there was no Jesus to be found.

Finally, Peter with Andrew, his brother, and two other fishermen friends, James and John, went out in search of their teacher. At last they found him in the woods on the hillside, and ran up, calling, "Please come, Master![2] Everybody is looking for you, and

[2]Another ancient name for teacher.

sick people are already sitting by the roadside begging for you to come."

"No," said Jesus firmly. "All they want is to be made well in their bodies. I did not come to Capernaum to be a medicine man. I must leave the town now, and go to other towns where they have not heard so much about sick people being made well. Perhaps then I can find people who are interested in other things — those of the heart and mind. Will any of you go with me, my friends? I need some helpers."

"But what could we do for you, Master?" asked Peter. "We are fishermen who do not know the holy books."

"There is much you could do, my friends," said Jesus. "You could go with me into a town and tell people where to come to hear me and when. If someone offered us lodging for the night, you could

*"Where is Jesus?
We're waiting for him."*

thank him heartily and tell us where we would be welcomed. We have found our people very generous to strangers. But if none offered hospitality, you could make camp outside the town and buy food and help in the cooking of our meals."

"But this would mean we would have to leave our homes and give up our fishing, and that is our only way of making a living. I don't see how we can do it," said John.

"Yes, I know," said Jesus. "I am asking a great deal of you. We shall have to learn to live one day at a time without being anxious about tomorrow. The foxes have holes and the birds have nests, but I no longer have a place of my own where I can lay down my head. We shall put our money into a common purse and spend it for the good of us all. At times we can work for our food, but often we shall have to be willing to accept the hospitality of kind-hearted people.

"You should count the cost, my friends, before you decide what to do. But if you stay with me long enough, you may learn to be teachers yourselves and so our work can go on and on. Whether you come with me or not, however, I see my own duty clearly. I must go forth to other cities."

Jesus' proposal was too serious a matter to be decided in a day. Again and again his four friends talked it over together and with their families, and over and over in their secret hearts they prayed for light. Finally the four men decided to leave everything and go with Jesus. Peter's mother-in-law and child were to be cared for by a friend who would take over Peter's and Andrew's fishing boat. James and John left their nets and boats to their father Zebedee. "Sons of Thunder" Jesus jokingly called these two men because they were often loud in their talk and very sure of themselves.

When the word passed around that Jesus was leaving town, others also asked for the privilege of joining the traveling band. Philip, a merchant from the important city of Bethsaida, on the other side of the lake, was a newly won enthusiast. Simon, one of the Patriots, strangely enough, joined the party in the hope that in the end he might persuade Jesus to become a rebel and help to overthrow the Roman rulers. What came as a surprise to everyone was that Jesus asked Matthew, the tax collector, to come with him. Matthew did not hesitate a moment, but gladly gave up his booth on the wharf and his well-paying job. It was a high honor for him to be a disciple of a great teacher, but it was not easy for the others of the band to take a tax collector into their inner circle. Jesus, however, knew Matthew could be trusted.

Judas, a young merchant from the town of Keriot near Jerusalem, also asked to join the group. He had traveled all over Galilee selling his rugs until he knew the towns like a book. He was doing well in his business, too, for he had a good head on his shoulders. But Jesus had so captured Judas' enthusiasm that he sold everything he had and put his money into the common purse. Judas thought, "Here at last is a leader who can save the nation." After a time there came to be twelve disciples who followed Jesus about.

There were women also who later joined the band. They were a great comfort, for they could do many things at which men's hands are clumsy; there was Susanna, for example, a favorite with everyone. But Mary Magdelene was different. When Jesus first knew her people called her a bad woman with seven evil spirits in her. There was Joanna also, the wife of a servant in King Herod's palace, of all things! The band that set forth with Jesus on this new venture was surely an uncommon company and those who did not know Jesus could not understand why he should have chosen some of its members.

At last the day came when they all left Capernaum to begin a tour of the towns of Galilee. As they went forth, they passed by the fishing wharf and the nets spread out on the grass and the rows of fish drying in the sun. For a moment, Andrew felt a secret wish that before too long he might return home and once more feel the thrill of pulling in a net bulging with flopping fishes. Peter's thoughts were different and he spoke them out loud. "These fish-ermen work hard early and late, they catch fish, sell fish, buy food, eat and sleep and go out again to catch more fish the next day and the next. There should be something more to living than just these things. What is it all for anyway?"

"It's not the kind of work a man does that makes the man, Peter. Did I say I would make you fishers of men? Remember, then, there is more to a man that what your eyes can see."

On hearing this the men walked briskly along wondering what Jesus meant. They felt vaguely that something great was in store for them all. But what was it?

10 The Crowd Shouts But Jesus Prays

NEWS that the teacher and his band were leaving Capernaum to go to Bethsaida spread from house to house. The hundreds who had come to honor and love Jesus as a teacher and friend were loath to see him go. They met on the street corners to share their disap-pointment one with another. They admitted that other cities might need him, but so did they.

Jesus had hoped to steal quietly away without being noticed. He had planned that Peter and Andrew and Philip with one of their fishing boats should meet him beside a beach a little to the east beyond the town. They would then sail to Bethsaida while the rest of the company would walk the few miles around the north end of the lake.

Philip was especially happy over the turn things had taken, for

Bethsaida was his home city. He said to Jesus: "I've been hoping ever since I first knew you to have the honor of giving you shelter under my own roof."

It was scarcely more than an hour's sail until the boat landed at the wharf well below the city of Bethsaida. Those who had not seen this provincial capital before were greatly surprised. Up the road leading from the wharf they walked until they reached the city wall. They saw stretching before them inside the gate a stately avenue lined on either side with Grecian pillars of white stone. The travelers felt they had entered a foreign land. The houses also were different from those in Capernaum. The people's faces and clothes were different, too. Only here and there among the passers-by did they see a Jew.

"The Roman Governor is a great admirer of the Greeks," Philip explained. He pointed out on the hillside the Governor's palace built after the Greek style. They could also see the large open-air theatre where Greek plays and dances were given. At the top of the avenue rising above all the other buildings of the city, its stones shining white and clean in the sunshine, stood the pillared temple to Zeus.[1]

Crowds of worshipers were going up the stately steps and into the sacred court beyond.

"This must be one of the Greek religious festivals," Philip went on. "I have often wondered what it is like beyond those pillars. But since we do not allow foreigners to enter the court in our temple in Jerusalem where the great altar stands, I have not thought it proper to intrude upon their worship."

"Has anyone ever told you of their customs?" asked Peter.

"Yes," Philip answered. "I have heard that their worship is much like our own except that they have in their Holy of Holies an image of Zeus. The people bring animals for sacrifice as we do. They also bring gifts of fruits and meal and wine. Priests lead in

---

[1]The Greek name for the Great Father of all gods.

their ceremonies; their choirs sing; musicians play, and youths and maidens dance."

"Have you had any dealings with these Greeks, Philip?" asked Peter again.

"Indeed I have, and often I have been in their homes. They have shrines there, too, in their own courtyards. Morning and evening every good Greek prays before his household shrine and brings some gift to lay on the altar. The Greeks are, as a rule, very religious people."

"More so than the Jews?" asked Andrew in surprise.

"Perhaps not, but I have seen much praying. I've been told that, on occasions when some great need is felt, men will sometimes stand before the altar the whole morning long praying continually. They repeat over and over the same prayer as if they thought that the more times they said the words, the more power the prayer would have with God."

As the men chatted, they continued on up a street to the left beyond the temple toward the Jewish quarter. There they found square mud and stone houses like those in Capernaum. There, also, they met the rest of the traveling company who had come by foot along the shore path. Arriving ahead of Jesus, they had spread the news of his coming. Men and women were already waiting on their doorsteps eager to invite one or more of the strangers to lodge with them. Others ran to meet the travelers and bowed reverently before the famous teacher. Boys and girls also came, singing as they ran. Mothers brought babes in their arms. Jesus touched their small heads lovingly. Sometimes he even took one of them up in his arms, talking quietly to him as he held him until the child, at first quite shy, began to smile back at Jesus in delight.

Some of Jesus' companions, however, were annoyed by the boys and girls who pushed their way into the crowds. One of the disciples complained to Jesus: "Tell the parents to send their children home."

But Jesus answered, "Let the children stay with us. Do not send them away. Do you not know that all of us need to become as little children if we would be in the Kingdom of God?"

When the children heard Jesus speak of them so kindly, their faces beamed. Here was a man who liked them; he believed they were worth something. The children liked Jesus in return.

By the time Jesus reached Philip's house and both of them had been welcomed by the wife and children, the crowd standing around filled the street completely from end to end. As Jesus looked about, he was surprised to find so many familiar faces. Many of his enthusiasts from Capernaum had evidently followed him by foot. There was no use trying to rest.

Therefore, without so much as a chance to eat, Jesus reluctantly bade Philip's family good-by. Joining the waiting throng he led them out of the city to an open pasture where they could all sit down together. Standing above them on a knoll, Jesus began once more to talk about the true Kingdom of God.

"Let us, for the time being, forget about struggling to gain our freedom from the Roman rule," he said. "God's time for that has not yet come."

"That's the same advice the Pharisees have long been giving us," protested one disappointed man.

"Is it not possible, Master, to be too patient?" asked another more timidly.

"The Romans have been cruel," burst out a bolder listener. "They have crucified or somehow killed hundreds of our choicest young men. It's time for action."

"Where's your faith in Almighty God?" called another. "You have been given wonderful power over the sick. God has shown his approval of you. He could also give you power to lead successfully an army against our enemies. Why not trust him?"

With each new protest the crowd shouted more loudly its approval.

"There are many of us already who would like the opportunity some day to crown you as our nation's king!"

What a wonderful thought! Many rose to their feet, waving their arms. "Hail Jesus!" "Arise, show your power!" Their voices rang out like trumpets blowing. "Let us have a king once more!" "Save us from our enemies!"

For many minutes the shouting filled the air; the people were afire with zeal, but through all the cheering Jesus stood unmoved. "Be quiet! Hold your peace!" Again and again he called, but there was no peace. When finally the people found that they were spending their enthusiasm to no purpose, their voices gradually, one by one, became still. Jesus began once more to speak.

"You know not what you are asking. I have come neither to destroy nor to kill. I have come to call our people to join a kingdom of righteousness — a kingdom we must join one by one, when we make our hearts right with God. Of what value will it be to free ourselves from our Roman rulers if in so doing we ourselves become more cruel, more greedy, and more filled with hatred? The coming of the Kingdom of God does not need to wait for our freedom as a nation. We Jews are still free to worship God according to our own consciences. We are still free to be kind and considerate of others. We are still free to treat our neighbors as we should like to be treated ourselves. We are still free to be honest and to learn the truth and to live in its light. The only king in such a Kingdom is God himself."

There was no uncertainty in Jesus' speaking. He knew what he believed. As he spoke, the crowd slowly grew quiet as men must do when deep in their hearts they feel the power of truth. They sat awed in the presence of a great man — greater than they had supposed. They could not bow their knees, but they could humble their hearts.

Only two in all the crowd could put their feelings into words.

"Blessed is the woman who gave you birth," called one.

"If everyone were like you, Master Jesus, the earth would be heaven," called another.

Jesus had not been speaking long — at least so it had seemed to all who were there, yet the day was now almost wholly spent. As the afternoon shadows crept over the hillside the air had begun to chill.

Two of his disciples stepped quietly up to Jesus and said: "Send the crowd away so that they can go into the town before it is too late and buy food for themselves."

But Jesus answered: "Is there need for them to go away? Can we not give them food?"

Philip answered in amazement: "Shall we go and buy two hundred shillings' worth of bread and give them to eat?"

"How many loaves are there here among us?" asked Jesus.

A lad, overhearing Jesus' question, stepped forward. "I have five loaves and two fishes. You may divide them."

Jesus smiled and, beckoning the boy to come nearer, he stood with uplifted arms and in a strong voice spoke a prayer of thankfulness to God.

For a few moments afterwards, there was complete silence. Men and women looked wonderingly at each other as if to say: "What are these few loaves and fishes among so many people?"

But presently others in the crowd brought out baskets and bags. All who had shared generously with those who had not. Before long, everyone had eaten heartily and still there was bread untouched. The crowd seemed refreshed and lighter in spirits as their friendliness grew.

Quietly Jesus called his disciples to him and asked that they leave, if possible, without being noticed and go back to the boat. "Sail slowly down the eastern shore of the lake. Do a little fishing perhaps and keep close to land. A little later I shall follow by the shore path and you can pick me up. But now I feel I must go somewhere further up the hill to pray for a while alone."

When the disciples had gone, Jesus bade the crowd good-by. Reluctantly yet gratefully they turned and started for their homes — some going to Bethsaida, and others walking back to Capernaum. Jesus walked on toward the hilltop alone.

It was late in the midst of a night dark with clouds when Jesus once more caught up with his companions. A heavy storm had risen on the lake, so that the sail on the boat had become useless and the rowing had been exceedingly heavy. The men were worn with the hard struggle against the waves. When finally, through the mists and rain, they caught sight of someone walking on the shore, they were frightened, thinking it might be a ghost. But Jesus called: "Be of good cheer! It is I! Be not afraid!" They recognized the familiar voice and gladly took him with them into the boat.

Jesus called: ". . . It is I! Be not afraid!"

When morning dawned, they found their way into a sheltered cove and came ashore. After cooking and eating a morning meal, they lingered on the rocks, basking restfully in the pleasant sunshine. The hard fight with the wind during the night and the experience with the crowd the day before had left the men solemn and awed. They had seen in Jesus a greatness that overpowered them. There had been times when they had felt close to him. Did he not eat and drink and sleep and work with them? Yet now they were almost afraid of him. They felt unworthy to be with him.

Before the storm had risen on the lake and while they had been leisurely fishing, the men had talked together about him. Why had he gone off alone to pray? They wondered. What did he do when he prayed? How did praying help him? Now that they had an opportunity to be with him alone, one of their number made the request they were all wishing to make. "Master, teach us to pray as you pray."

Jesus was touched. He saw in their faces the earnest longings within. But what could he tell them? It was not easy to set out before them the secret treasure of his inmost life.

"Do not be a hypocrite when you pray. Be sincere. There are those who love to stand and pray in the synagogue or who are happy if the hour of prayer comes when they are on a street corner. They want to be seen praying. They want people to say: 'What a good man this is! So faithful in his prayers!' If that is the value one desires from praying, then one can find that reward.

"When you pray go into your own private room and, having shut the door, pray to your Father in secret. He who sees the secrets within your hearts will reward you.

"When you pray, do not do as those foreigners of whom we heard yesterday. They think their requests may not be granted unless they repeat the same prayers over and over many times. Do not be like them. Your prayers do not require words at all, for your Father knows what you have need of before you ask him.

"And be not afraid that God will give you something harmful rather than something good. Suppose your son asks a loaf of bread of you, will you give him a stone? Of if he shall ask for a fish, will you give him a snake? Or if he shall ask for an egg, will you give him a scorpion? If you then, being sinful, know how to give good gifts to your children, how much more shall your heavenly Father give good things to them that ask him?"

"It comforts us to hear you speak in this way," said John thoughtfully. Others, however, were still unsatisfied.

"But, Master," pleaded Peter, "give us a prayer that we can say. We need a guide. We need to know the words to use so that we shall pray about the things we should."

Jesus hesitated. He had just said that the words themselves were not important. He did not wish to have his friends copy his prayers. Their prayers should be their own. Their words should express truly their own purposes and desires. But his disciples pressed him until at last Jesus consented to suggest a few guiding thoughts.

"Address God simply — but reverently:

Our Father, Hallowed be thy name.

"Remind yourselves of the true kingdom of God. Make a new purpose to let God rule your own life:

Thy kingdom come. Thy will be done on earth as it is in heaven.

"Acknowledge God as the giver of your daily blessings, and feel secure in the thought that if you first of all seek righteousness, God will enable you to obtain the needful food:

Give us day by day our daily bread.

"Then look at your own faults and look also at the faults of others which you may not yet have forgiven. Will you be patient with them and forgive? Then pray:

Forgive us our sins for we ourselves have forgiven every-
one that has sinned against us.

"Then seek for help in keeping away from the things that will tempt you again to evil. Purpose not to repeat your faults:

And bring us not into temptation but deliver us from evil."

After Jesus had made these few suggestions, no one spoke; for a long while the little company sat in silence. Each within himself was praying in secret before God.

It was a morning they never forgot.

11 *Hannah Is Sick with Fear*

ARRIVING just at sundown within the gates of another town, Jesus and his friends found their way to the market place, where they hoped that some good man, seeing they were strangers, would invite them to his house for the night.

Only a few stragglers were still lingering about the market. They were gathering up their unsold wares in bundles or putting them in carts to wheel off home. Jesus and his friends sat down quietly on some benches near by and watched. Presently they heard the murmur of voices and the patter of many feet on the stone pavements. A large company began to fill the market place. Its leader could be distinguished from the others by the purple cloak that hung from his shoulders and the sky-blue tassels that dangled from its corners.

"Another rabbi!" whispered Peter.

"Yes," said John. "He's going to be teaching here tonight. Let us sit and listen to him."

Jesus was pleased with this opportunity, for although he knew that there were other traveling teachers in Galilee he seldom was able to sit by and listen to them without being noticed.

Soon the people seated themselves on stools, benches and tables, and the rabbi began.

"Your reward in heaven will depend on the pains you take now to keep all the laws of God, and of these laws none is more important than the fourth commandment, to keep the Sabbath day holy. 'Whosoever doeth any work on the Sabbath day, he shall surely be put to death.' These áre the words of Moses. You remember the story of the man who disregarded this law and went out on the Sabbath to gather sticks for building a fire. Did he find forgiveness merely by praying for it afterwards? No, not at all! At the command of Moses he was led out of the camp, and all the people stoned him until he died."

The rabbi spoke sternly. He meant his listeners should know that it was a serious matter to do work on the Sabbath day. There must be no buying or selling, no carrying of a burden from one house to another, no cooking, no starting of fires, no putting out of fires, no work in the fields, no picking of fruits, no dancing; no boy should be allowed to climb a tree or swim in the lake, nor should one even take a walk into the country farther from home than two thousand cubits[1] — a Sabbath day's journey.

The listening crowd stared at the teacher with dull, uninterested

_____
[1] A cubit was 1½ feet long.

eyes. What, then, was there left to do on the Sabbath? Fortunately a few were still courageous enough to speak.

"But how big must a thing be to be called a burden?" asked a man with a long beard sitting in the front row. "Surely we may still carry about many small things."

"Our rabbis have been very careful and particular to tell us just how big a Sabbath-day burden may be. One says that a single fig is a burden forbidden on the Sabbath; another says, 'Enough milk to make one swallow.'"

"If we followed such extreme rules," said a young man standing against a booth at the side of the crowd, "the very day itself would become a burden to us."

"Not so, sir," answered the rabbi quickly. "It is written that the Sabbath shall be a day of delight and rest to the spirit."

"My brother's son fell on a Sabbath day two weeks ago and broke his leg," began a woman with a nursing babe in her lap. "I ran to the home of the town doctor to urge him to come quickly and strap the leg to a board to stop the boy's crying. But the doctor would not come because it was the Sabbath. Why should a kindness like that be forbidden on the Sabbath?"

"If the boy's life had been in danger, the doctor should have come," said the rabbi, "but if the boy was merely in pain and the leg could wait until the next day to be strapped, the doctor was right in refusing to come. Even a doctor must not do his work of healing on the Sabbath."

This was a hard saying. The woman tightened her lips and shook her head vigorously.

As the rabbi continued to speak, the crowd sat in timid quietness. They hid their doubts behind their wrinkled brows. Could these commands be from God? But they did not dare question the words of so learned a rabbi.

A hesitant voice was heard from the back of the crowd. "A rumor of another teacher has gone around the town. His name is Jesus, I believe, and he comes from Nazareth. They say he has never studied with the great teachers in Jerusalem, but he is popular with the people; crowds follow after him and hang on his words. Now this Jesus, it is said, takes pleasure in openly breaking these laws. One Sabbath, for instance, as he and his followers were walking through a wheat field, they were seen plucking the wheat from the stalks near by, rubbing the grains in their hands, blowing away the chaff and eating what they had gathered. That was working on the Sabbath, was it not, sir?"

"Certainly! They sinned greatly, for they broke the law of the Sabbath on three counts. They reaped, threshed and winnowed the grain. All three kinds of work have been definitely forbidden."

At this point, Jesus could hold back no longer. He rose from his bench and he said, "I am the person of whom you have just spoken. My friends and I reached here this evening just as our honored rabbi began teaching. I have something to say in answer to your charge, but I do not deny that we gathered and ate the handfuls of wheat on the Sabbath day. We were hungry and tired, for no one that day had invited us to supper with them. Have you not read what David did on the Sabbath day? How when he and his company were hungry, he went even into the tent of meeting and took the holy bread from the altar and ate it and gave also to them that were with him? I say to you, there are things more important than merely following all the small rules our rabbis have made."

"You have said enough, sir," interrupted the rabbi sternly. "Who are you to exalt yourself above our learned teachers?"

With these words the crowd began muttering. No one's voice could be heard above the din. They rose and walked away, each to his own home. Who was right? How could they know?

Aside from Jesus' little company, one man, a weaver, lingered in the market place.

"Peace be to you, Rabbi Jesus," he said, bowing low before

him. "Will you and your friends honor me by spending the night in our home?"

So, once more, the little teaching band was cared for, but not for one night only. It was nearly a week that they spent in the town, and Jesus had many opportunities for teaching. Sometimes the people came to the weaver's home. Sometimes they gathered on the grassy bank of a stream that ran near the town.

Then came the afternoon before the sunset that marked the beginning of the next Sabbath. The weaver, having finished the rug on which he had been working, said to Jesus: "Now that the heat of the day is past, let us sit together on the roof." Jesus was pleased with this chance to have a leisurely talk. So he seated himself near the low wall that enclosed the roof where he could look down on the people passing on the street below. He began asking the weaver for their names and for stories about them. What about the potter and the carpenter down the street, and the seller of figs in whose shop Jesus had been that day? What sort of man was the teacher of the synagogue school? And how many boys had completed their studies there? Were all the Pharisees in the town as strict about the Sabbath as the other visiting rabbi had been?

The talkative weaver did not notice how the time was flying as he told story after story for his guest.

"And who is that stooped old woman hobbling down the street just now, leaning so heavily on her cane?" asked Jesus. "Has she a story, too, my friend?"

Leaning over the wall to make sure whom Jesus meant, the weaver answered, "Ah, that is Hannah, the gloomy widow. The Devil got into her many years ago and she's been queer ever since. It all began when her only son died. She was a pretty woman once, sprightly and gay. Her son was proud of her. But he left her and joined one of the guerrilla bands that are fighting the Romans. Through all the long months he was away from home, his mother prayed one prayer — that her boy might return safe and well.

"When finally he did come home, he surprised his mother by appearing on the Sabbath day, but Hannah had no warm food in the house and she had neglected her fire. Yet she was determined her son should not wait until sundown for a good, hot meal. So Hannah built a fire and baked some cakes, saying in her heart, 'God will forgive me this once.' When the neighbors learned of what she had done, they scolded her, saying, 'You have done wrong, Hannah. God will surely punish you.'

"Later, Hannah's son returned to his hiding place with the guerrillas and on their next raid he was killed. It was but two weeks after his home-coming. Even the ruler of the synagogue accused Hannah and said it was all her fault. God was punishing her for her sin. The poor woman has never stood up straight since that day. Her face grew old and haggard in a week's time. People are afraid of her for they say the Devil has bound her. And Hannah scarcely speaks to anyone."

As the weaver finished his long story, he turned squarely around. "What do you say about such things as these, Rabbi Jesus?" he asked.

Before there was time for an answer, a trumpet blast was heard. Yonder, standing on the roof of the synagogue, they saw a man with a trumpet before his mouth. A second blast came, and then a third. As the echo of the final blast died away, the two men rose, bowed their heads and prayed: "It is the Sabbath. Blessed art thou, O Lord God of the world, who hast made this holy day and given us the commandments for keeping it."

At that moment, everyone else in the town was praying, too — on street corners, in shops, in homes or wherever people happened to be. After the hush of the first solemn moments, faint lights began to flicker out through doorway after doorway as little Sabbath lamps were lighted to shine on supper tables all over the town.

The weaver and the traveling teacher and his companions now joined the rest of the family at the Sabbath evening meal in the

"It is the Sabbath."

room below. The weaver's wife served them kindly, knowing well
that she had done her Sabbath duty. Had she not finished all the
cooking that needed to be done until the following evening at
sunset when the Sabbath would be over?

In the morning and all through the Sabbath day, a hundred and
one rules kept the town quiet and inactive. The one big event of
the day was the morning service in the synagogue. On this particular morning the House of Meeting would be packed, for all the
town was curious. Jesus of Nazareth would speak, they were sure
of that, and something stirring was likely to happen.

At the call of the trumpet, therefore, the streets were filled with
men and boys hurrying to the House of Meeting. Women and girls
followed properly, behind their brothers and fathers. While the

men and boys entered the central door of the synagogue and sat down in the main room, the women and girls climbed the steps to a side door and sat down in a low gallery behind a lattice.

The lattice was low enough so that the women could see over it to the high platform in the center of the room, but high enough so that the men sitting on the benches below could not see the women's faces. The women could see also the light of the sacred lamp that hung before the beautiful curtain at the far end of the room — the blue, gold, scarlet and purple curtain that hid the sacred ark where the scrolls of the Law were kept. They could watch the faces of the rulers of the synagogue who sat in a row of seats on a platform in front of the curtain. They could see also the new teacher, Jesus of Nazareth, sitting beside them.

On this Sabbath morning, as on every other Sabbath morning for years, there sat behind the lattice the bent, sorrowful figure of Hannah. As the congregation rose to repeat the opening prayer, she rose and her lips moved with the others.

One of the solemn-looking men, sitting at the back of the room, stepped behind the beautiful curtain. Returning with a big scroll in his hand, he walked to the platform in the center of the room and read a long reading from the scroll. Hannah did not lift her head or seem to hear. A second man from among the men in front of the curtain read a second reading. Then the congregation stood and repeated another long prayer. Hannah's lips said the words, but her thoughts were far away.

After the prayer there was a moment of silence. All the people looked expectantly at Jesus. Nor were they to be disappointed. Dressed in his plain, rough, everyday cloak, but with a prayer shawl hanging over his head and shoulders, he stood a moment in silence behind the reading desk. He had no scroll in his hand. He did not read the sayings of any learned teacher of the past. In fact, he began talking to the people so simply and so naturally that some of them were surprised. He was saying things he himself had thought through, and he was in earnest. For the first time, Hannah lifted her eyes and began watching Jesus over the lattice as he began to speak.

"Our teachers of old have given us many laws to obey. Who is there among us who has counted them all? Neither can any man learn them all. Nor do our teachers agree among themselves. One tells us one thing, and another something different, regarding the laws. As for keeping the Sabbath, they have made it a day for re-membering the things we cannot do, rather than a day in which to live with joy and gladness before God. They have forgotten that there are but two important commandments: *Thou shalt love the Lord thy God with all thy heart, and with all thy soul, and with all thy mind, and with all thy strength; Thou shalt love thy neighbor as thy self.* These are the two great commandments for us to re-member. It is better to forget the thousands of little rules than to forget the important ones. I ask you: Which can be more pleasing in God's sight — for a widow to love her son and bake him some fresh cakes when he comes home from fighting, or for her not to build a fire on the Sabbath day and not to have a meal to give him?"

As Jesus spoke he looked up at the women's gallery. Hannah had lifted her eyes and was watching him in wonder and surprise.

For a moment Jesus could not speak. He turned and looked at the men on the benches behind him. He seemed undecided. Finally, straightening himself as a man does who has a hard thing to do, he said, "A good deed is waiting to be done this Sabbath day."

There was an uneasy stirring of men on their benches. The rulers sitting before the curtain looked at one another wondering what this new teacher might do next.

Jesus looked up once more at the women's gallery, and called: "Hannah! I have been told the story of your years of bitterness. I understand why you have believed that the Devil was allowed to punish you. But if you had only known the truth you would have known that God has been loving you all these years. He could not have been angry with you for your love of your son. Whether or not you built a fire and baked the cakes did not really matter. Come down from behind the lattice, Hannah, that I may give you my hand."

The voice seemed to Hannah like a call from heaven. She could not disobey. Slowly she hobbled down the stairs and into the main room where all the men could stare at her ugly, bent body. Some of the men before the curtain turned their faces away.

Jesus stepped down from the platform to meet Hannah. Putting his hands on her shoulders, he looked tenderly upon her bowed head. "Hannah," he said softly. "You are not a bad woman. Look up! Be glad once more!"

The sure tone in Jesus' voice gave the woman courage. She tried to lift herself up. She looked straight into Jesus' eyes. What was this he was saying? Hadn't she really caused her son's death? Why, then, had he died? Jesus guessed her thoughts. He spoke again to her. "Your baking of cakes on the Sabbath had nothing to do with your son's dying. He risked his life for his country. Those who take up the sword often perish with the sword. Hannah, you have never needed God's forgiveness for your deed that day long ago."

Then Hannah burst out with a loud shout: "God be praised!" She felt like a prisoner loosed from his chains. She was no longer afraid of God or man. Without her knowing it she was standing up straighter. A new look came into her wrinkled face. Like a little child, she knew not how to say "Thank you!" She walked back up the stairs to her seat in the gallery behind the lattice. She carried her cane but she did not seem to lean on it. And all the while she kept saying to herself, "God be praised! God be praised!"

The chief ruler of the synagogue, however, rose in anger from his seat. Work had been done on the Sabbath day, and that in the synagogue by one who claimed to be a teacher, and it had all been done for the sake of a sinful woman. The ruler of the synagogue would have none of it. "There are six days in the week when men ought to work," he cried. "In them come and be healed, but not on the Sabbath day."

Jesus turned and faced the ruler and the other men sitting before the curtain. His face was flushed because of the battle he knew he had begun.

"You hypocrites!" he said. "Does not each one of you on the Sabbath day loose his ox or his ass from the stall and lead him away to watering? Ought not this woman, a daughter of Abraham, who has been bound, lo, these many years, to be loosed from this bondage on the day of the Sabbath?"

The chief ruler of the synagogue could make no answer, and neither could the other men before the curtain; they hung their heads in silence.

Once out of the synagogue when the service was over, the men who had sat on the benches and the women who had been behind the lattice went wild with enthusiasm. As Hannah walked home, her neighbors were no longer afraid to talk to her. It was a cause for wonder just to see her smile.

"You are a Man of God," said the weaver to Jesus when once again they were in his home. "You did a miracle today. Only a Man of God could do such wonderful things."

"I did nothing but speak the truth," said Jesus. "The truth made the woman free."

But the weaver did not understand. He did not know how powerful *Truth* is or how great is the man who sees it clearly. Like most of the others who had seen what had happened, he thought there must be some sort of God-given magic just in the *words* Jesus had said. Exaggerated rumors spread from town to town up and down the lake.

12 Jesus Faces His Accusers

THE leaders of the synagogues of the country were greatly puzzled to know what to do about Jesus. Some said: "He is not a good man because he does not keep the Sabbath day holy." Others said: "How can a bad man do so much good as Jesus is doing?" Those men who belonged to the society of the Pharisees were especially disturbed. Their ideas about being good and those of Jesus simply could not live comfortably side by side.

It was not merely because Jesus seemed to be careless about obeying the Sabbath laws that some began to oppose him. It was also because of his attitude toward people whom the Pharisees regarded as disreputable citizens. Jesus was back once more in Capernaum and it distressed the synagogue leaders to be reminded again of the honor shown to Matthew, the former tax collector. A man in such a business they regarded as a traitor and a robber. They had not forgotten the big feast Matthew had given in Jesus' honor and the other traitors and foreigners and thieves and even women with bad reputations who had been there.

The Pharisees taught that one-tenth of all food raised should be set aside for the temple. Also, it was forbidden to Jews to eat certain kinds of foods that foreigners ate freely. All meat had to be prepared according to the laws in the Bible. The Pharisees said that when the laws were not obeyed the food was "unclean," and the persons who ate of it would also become "unclean" — that is, they would become unfit to go to the synagogue or to the temple to pray. The Pharisees said it was unworthy of a teacher to associate so freely with such people and to eat foods not properly pre-

94

pared. To Jesus, however, obeying such rules seemed less important than helping people who were really hungry in their hearts for love and understanding.

In spite of these criticisms of Jesus, some of the Pharisees held him in high honor. They saw a nobility and a sincerity in him that they respected. One happy day, one of their number had the courage to invite Jesus to his own home for a feast. Jesus was glad to go.

As the guests were gathering, Jesus noticed how some began to choose the seats of honor nearest the host. But when the host himself arrived, he had to ask certain ones to give up their seats to the friends for whom he had planned the special honors. The disappointed ones were envious and hurt.

When the dinner was over and the company were sitting leisurely chatting, the host invited Jesus to talk a while to them. Because of what he had seen, there was but one matter that seemed important for the moment. It was a delicate subject to speak of, yet Jesus was not one to shrink from being outspoken and honest. In his usual open manner he spoke out his mind.

"When you are invited to a wedding feast, do not sit down in the chief seat, lest possibly a more honorable man than you be invited to sit there. He who gave the feast shall then come and say to you, 'Give this man your place.' Then you will be humiliated and you will have to go to the lowest place.

"But when you are invited to a feast, go and sit down in the least honorable place so that when your host comes he may perhaps come to you and say, 'Friend, go up higher.' Then you shall be honored in the presence of all who sit at the table with you. *For everyone that exalteth himself shall be humbled; and he that humbleth himself shall be exalted.*"

Jesus then turned to his host and talked especially to him. "When you give a dinner or a supper, my friend, do not invite your friends, or your family, or your relatives, or your rich neighors, in the hope that they will give you an invitation to their homes in return. You will then receive as much as you have given. That will be your reward.

"But when you give a feast invite the poor, the maimed, the lame, the blind; and you shall be blessed, because they will have no way of returning your kindness. *It is more blessed to give than to receive.*"

Such suggestions as these seemed strange to the guests at the dinner. Should Jesus' host be offended or amused? After all, what would people say if he gave such a party as Jesus proposed?

Altogether it was not surprising that the Pharisees did not agree regarding Jesus, and that many among them were antagonistic toward him. Some found that their own reputations were being hurt because of Jesus' teachings. They began, therefore, to plan ways by which they might even the score with Jesus.

It was decided that a special meeting in the synagogue should be called on a weekday afternoon. There they would present their complaints and there they would give Jesus an opportunity to answer for himself.

When the day for the meeting came, such crowds gathered in the hall that every bench was filled. Jesus and the chief Pharisees sat in a row on the platform, while the people in front of them waited excitedly to see what would happen. One by one the Pharisees rose and presented their complaints.

"Jesus has been careless about obeying the laws of the Sabbath," said the first accuser. "This alone is enough to make him unfit to be a teacher of the laws of God. You have heard again and again how he has healed the sick on the Sabbath day. You have heard also how he and his friends harvested, threshed and winnowed wheat as they walked through a field on the Sabbath."

"More than this!" said another accuser. "Jesus is never seen fasting. Instead he goes about from home to home eating heartily every day, while the rest of us fast, sometimes two whole days a week! How can God hear the prayers of such a man who denies himself so little in order to make his prayers heard? Some people have even called him a glutton in his eating."

On hearing this, Jesus' face flushed. He knew the complaint was unfair, but how could he prove it?

"There's something even worse than eating and drinking," interrupted still another. "This man associates with bad people. He accepts their hospitality. He eats at their tables and sleeps in their homes. He's been making friends with robbers and traitors and bad women. He seems to enjoy their boisterous feasts and drinks their wine too freely to be proper for a teacher of the Law."

Then came a high-pitched voice from the back of the room. "It's not only that he likes this gay life of the rabble so well; but when he is in their homes he takes no pains to teach them to obey the laws. If a servant does not pass a basin around before the meal is served so that guests may wash their hands, Jesus himself will eat without washing his hands! And how does he know when he is in such homes whether the food he eats has been properly cooked according to the Law of Moses? Our teachers have taught that to eat such food is like eating poison. It poisons the soul as well as the body. How can we honor such a man, I ask you?"

During all this time Jesus watched the faces of the people in front of him. Here and there he caught friendly glances that gave him comfort.

But the complaints continued. "You can know a person by the company he keeps. This saying is as old as King David; did he not say that the good man standeth not among sinners, nor does he sit in the seat of the scornful?"

Then a handsome young fellow added in a sure tone of voice still another point. "Our society believes we must keep separate from those who do not obey the law in order to keep ourselves pure. We cannot make friends with bad people and at the same time be good ourselves. Their food, their pots and pans, their cups and saucers, their clothes, their houses — all these things are 'unclean,'

because their owners are careless or refuse to do the duties that have been commanded us."

At these words, the people shifted uneasily on their benches and murmured, shaking their heads in protest. Jesus could feel their anger rising like a hot wind from a furnace.

Then a stooped and honored old man rose. Solemnly he presented the last and greatest complaint.

"When these sinners are ready to repent and turn and obey the laws along with us, we will gladly take them in with us and

"I am not calling the righteous, but sinners to repent."

teach them; for like God we should be long-suffering and forgiving. But so long as God himself does not forgive these wicked people, why should we? We cannot do more than God."

Then were the people afraid. Some hung their heads as if ashamed; some wiped tears from their eyes; while others looked up at Jesus like timid children hoping for a father's tenderness.

But Jesus was not frightened. He brought forth his thoughts as clearly as the tones of a bell ringing from a tower.

"Hear me, all of you," he called, "and understand; there is

99

nothing from outside a person that can go into him and make him bad. Badness grows from within. It is only what comes out of a man's own heart and mind that can make him bad. It is not the kind of meat you eat, or the kind of drinks you drink, that can make you bad. It is not the things you touch with your hands, or the clothes you wear or the cups you handle that can make you bad. Evil thoughts cannot come out of meat and clothes. It is only from *inside* — from the heart — that evil thoughts and desires can come, and these alone can make you bad. Out of the heart comes the wish to steal or to harm another person or to kill. Out of the heart come feelings of coveting and pride and hate and the desire for selfish pleasures regardless of the needs of others. These things that come from within — that you can neither see nor touch — that come out of yourself — these alone can make you bad."

Turning to the Pharisees themselves, Jesus said, "Some of you are like monuments over men's graves. They look clean and beautiful, but underneath are dead men's bones. In the same manner, some of you appear to be very good, but inwardly you are full of pretence and evil desires. You are like housekeepers who wash thoroughly the outsides of cups and bowls, but leave the inside dirty."

Offended at his words, the men on the platform became restless. The leader rose to speak, but Jesus had more he wished to say.

"The 'bad' people you talk of are like the sick," he went on. "They need care and helpfulness and love. They will not be made well by punishings or by our keeping proudly aloof from them. I think of myself as being like a doctor — not of men's bodies, but of their souls. A doctor does not go to call in the homes of those who think themselves well and have no need of his care. He goes to the homes of the sick. So I also go to the homes of sinners. I am not calling the righteous, but sinners to repent."

"Enough said, sir! You have condemned yourself," said the chief Pharisee sternly. Quickly he dismissed the crowd.

But many of the people heard Jesus' words with a secret gladness and went out of the House of Meeting with light hearts, eager to hear more from this man.

When Jesus' friends were again alone with him, they told him that the Pharisees had taken offense at what he had said. It was dangerous to make enemies of men so highly honored and so influential among the people. If these Pharisees continued to dislike his teachings, they could make Jesus a "nobody" in quick time.

But Jesus did not seem to be concerned about himself at all. He simply said, "Let the Pharisees alone. They are like blind men leading other blind men. Sooner or later they will both fall into a a ditch."

But his friends wondered. How can Jesus be so confident? Does he think God will rescue him from danger by some special miracle? Time would tell.

13 Let Us Make Merry And Be Glad

THE public meeting in the synagogue did not end the discussions about making friends with bad people. There were those who wanted to hear Jesus explain it all again. Even though he had offended the Pharisees in the synagogue, there was something about him that kept even the teachers wanting more. Some, however, jealous of his popularity, came to listen in order to find fault with him.

To Jesus it was natural to be friendly. He liked people of all sorts, even those whom others called "bad." He could not feel differently, and he believed that God himself felt the same way he did about people. Sitting in the market place at eventide with a crowd about him, Jesus told three stories to show more clearly what he thought.

"Suppose there was a shepherd among you," Jesus began, "who had one hundred sheep in his flock. One day as he was leading them up a hillside and over a mountain to find grass, one of the flock wandered off from the rest without his knowing it. Suppose that later, toward evening, as the shepherd was nearing the sheep-fold, he counted the sheep and, to his surprise, found that one was missing. Would he not put the ninety and nine sheep safely into the fold and close the gate, and then go back to the hillside and over the mountain to hunt for the sheep that was lost?

"When at last he found it, would he not lay the sheep over his shoulder and with a song in his heart walk back to the fold? And would he not call his neighbors and friends together that evening and say to them, 'Rejoice with me, for I have found my sheep that was lost!' I say unto you, that even so there shall be more joy in heaven over one sinner that repents, than over ninety and nine so-called 'good' persons who feel no need to repent.

"Or let us imagine another story," said Jesus. "A certain woman had ten pieces of silver which she kept carefully hidden in her house; but on a certain day she found one piece missing. The woman, therefore, lit a lamp and as she swept the house she looked carefully everywhere, even into each dark corner, until she found the piece that had been lost.

"When she had found the money again, she called together her friends and neighbors, saying, 'Rejoice with me, for I have found the piece of money I had lost.' Even so, I say unto you, God rejoices over one sinner that repents."

When Jesus had finished these two stories, the crowd sat quietly. Some looked dreamily out over the market place. Others stroked their beards to help themselves think. What was the point of the stories? "Why try to obey the laws if God is so happy over those who flout them?" asked a bold young fellow. But before any-one else could put his puzzled thoughts into words Jesus began a third story.

"A certain man and his two sons lived together on a large farm where many servants were continually at their beck and call. Even additional laborers were hired by the day to help gather the har-vests. Although the boys had everything money could buy, the younger son grew restless and discontented with his lot. He wanted to travel, to see the world and to be free to do as he pleased.

"Now it was the law of the land that the oldest son, on the death of the father, should be given two-thirds of all the property. Knowing this, the younger son figured out that his older brother would inherit the farm and that his own portion would be largely in money. He, therefore, began planning how he might begin life on his own in some more exciting place. So one day he went to his father and said, 'I wish you would give me right now the portion of your wealth that is to be mine when you die, so that I may set out for myself to make my living in my own way.'

"Seeing that his son could no longer be satisfied on the farm, the father finally consented and divided his wealth, giving the older son the entire farm and giving the younger his smaller share of the wealth in the form of money and presents. Not many days after, the younger son gathered all his things together, said good-by to his father and brother, and set forth alone to go to a far country to seek his fortune.

"When at last the young man reached a country that pleased his fancy and where he found the kind of people he enjoyed, he stayed. By a lavish use of his money, he made many friends. For a while he was exceedingly happy. As the months passed by, how-ever, he became more and more wasteful and extravagant in his spending; and before he realized his folly, he found he had spent all his money.

"Just at this time a great misfortune came upon the people of the country where he was living — the usual rains did not fall and harvests were poor. The rich soon became poor, and the poor began to starve for lack of food, and the young son, once so lavish with his money, found himself with nothing at all. Finally, he went to a certain citizen of the country and asked for work on his farm. As a result the young man was sent out into the fields to help feed the pigs. Many were the times when he would have been glad to fill his hungry stomach with the bean pods the pigs ate, for no man gave him anything better. For weeks he was always painfully hungry. As a result he became so discouraged that he almost lost his mind.

"At last he pulled himself together and tried to think reasonably. 'My father at home has many servants with him always; and besides he is able to hire laborers to work by the day whenever he needs them. All these servants have food to eat and even to spare. Here I am, his own son, and I am starving to death. I will leave this place. I will go back to my father and I will say to him: "Father, I have sinned against God and in your sight; I am no more worthy to be called your son. Just take me in as one of your hired servants. That is all I ask." '

"Then the young man arose and left the country to which he had gone and returned to his father's house. While he was still far off his father saw him, and was filled with pity for him. He ran at once to meet his son and threw his arms around his neck and kissed him.

"The son began to say what he had planned to say when he would again see his father: 'Father, I have sinned against God and in your sight. I am no longer worthy to be called your son.' But he could go no further for his father interrupted him and called to one of his servants: 'Bring the best robe and put it on my son, and put a ring on his hand and shoes on his feet. Then run find the fat calf we have been keeping for such a time as this. Kill it and make a feast for us that we may make merry; for this my son has been dead and now he is alive again! He was lost and now he is found!'

"As the news of the younger son's home-coming spread around the farm, the entire household began to make merry. Pipers brought out their pipes, and harpists their harps. Soon the entire household were dancing and singing.

"While all these things were happening, the older son was far off in the field working. As evening came on and he drew near home, he heard the music and the singing, and saw the dancing groups in the courtyard. Calling one of his servants to him, he asked, 'What do these things mean?'

"The servant told him: 'Your brother has come home, and your father is so happy that he had the fat calf killed, and a feast is being prepared because your brother has come home safe and sound. Your father says: "He has been lost, but now he is found."'

"On hearing this news the older brother was angry, and would not even go into the house to see his brother. When the father

an at once to
his son

heard of his elder son's anger, he came out of the house to find him and begged his son to come in and welcome his brother back.

"But the older son answered his father sharply. 'All these many years, I have lived with you and worked for you. I have never disobeyed you in all my life. And you never killed even a young goat just for me that I might make merry with my friends. Yet immediately when your younger son comes back home, after wasting your money in foolish living with bad people, you kill for him the fat calf!'

"Surprised that his son should feel hurt, the father said: 'My son, you have been with me always and everything I have is yours. I gave it all to you before your brother left home when I divided my wealth between you. But now your brother has come back, repenting of his wrongdoing. He is like a man who has been dead but now is alive. He has been lost but now he is found. It is right for us to make merry and be glad.' "

As Jesus ended the story, he said, "Just as this father rejoiced over his son's home-coming, even so God rejoices over even one sinner who repents. Like this father, God is ready to forgive him all his wrongdoing even before he asks him."

For some minutes after Jesus had spoken, not a voice or a sound of any kind could be heard. Those who had felt themselves despised and rejected by the Pharisees, now sat upright with eyes gleaming. They had understood and were glad. But others began to shift nervously in their seats. Presently these broke the stillness with excited arguments. It was painful to be shaken out of their old ways of thinking.

"The elder brother was justified in his anger," said a Pharisee emphatically. "If God is as easy as that with sinners, he is not a God of justice!"

"Here! Here!" shouted another. "Wickedness cannot be so easily overlooked. The one who sins must be punished for his wrongdoing!"

"It's a soft religion!" said a stern old man in disdain. "Very pleasant for the sinners! But who would not choose the gay life of sin for a while if he knew that he would be rewarded so beautifully in the end?"

"You're destroying the Law! You should not be allowed to set yourself up as a rabbi," exclaimed a young merchant. "Or else you never went to school long enough to learn what the laws are."

"That's the trouble!" shouted another, with a shrug of the shoulder. "This man is from Nazareth. Never yet has a respectable teacher come out of that commonplace town!"

Then the teacher of the synagogue school stood up and faced Jesus squarely.

"The Scriptures are very clear on this point, sir," he said. "He who sins shall die. That is the foundation stone on which the whole Law is built. Man's one big problem is: How may I escape this punishment? And the laws explain the ways in great detail. They are prayer, fasting, giving alms to the poor, bringing offerings to the temple, keeping the Sabbath day holy. Without these no man can be saved from punishment either in this world or in the world to come after death. But by your teachings, Jesus of Nazareth, you would do away with all our laws and ceremonies! To be sure, God will forgive the sinner if he sincerely repents. But it cannot be that God rejoices more over a person who has sinned than over all those who, day and night all their lives, faithfully keep his commandments."

By this time the crowds were becoming restless. The people saw that once more disputing was to begin. It seemed now that every talk Jesus gave ended in a dispute.

But Jesus was unruffled and ready with his answer. "Honored Rabbi," he said respectfully, "the Scriptures also teach that God is long suffering and full of mercy and loving-kindness. Have you not read what David said? 'The sacrifices of God are a broken spirit: a broken and a contrite heart, O God, thou wilt not despise.' In

saying this did David make all sacrifices of no value? Not at all.
He was saying what I am saying — that more important than all
burnt offerings and sacrifices is 'truth in the inward parts.' No, I
have not come to destroy the laws. I have come to give them their
true meaning."

Hearing these words, many of those listening were comforted.
Even those who were unfriendly toward Jesus had nothing more
they could say. And those who had been unhappy outcasts from
the synagogue, but who were now yearning for everything good
that their hearts could feel and their hands could do — these people without honors or schooling rose with light hearts and thanked
the good teacher. They felt encouraged rather than scolded.

In a short while some began pushing the benches and tables
back to clear the market place. The crowd started singing, and to
the music of flutes and cymbals they danced merrily.

14 Two Kinds of Kingdoms

ON a mountaintop overlooking the Dead Sea stood the grim
fortress of Machaerus. Behind its stone walls lived a lonely prisoner, the once famous Hermit Preacher, John the Baptizer. In
the hot sun in an open court, day after day, he sat helpless with his
feet held in stocks; or else he was left to brood for long hours alone,
chained to the wall of a dingy cell. A few faithful friends had been
bringing him his daily food. They had tried to comfort him with
the hope that he might soon be freed to preach again and to call
his people to repent.

Not far off on another height rose the castle of Herod Antipas, the Governor of Galilee and Perea. In its splendid banquet hall, Herod and a large assembly of his courtiers were feasting and drinking wine. For their entertainment, Herod's graceful young stepdaughter, Salome, was dancing. When she had given her bow the guests applauded loudly. Herod, drunk with wine and thinking only of the moment's pleasure, exclaimed, "Daughter, ask anything you wish and I will give it to you!" Salome, surprised and flattered, asked that she might consult her mother, Herod's newly wedded wife. It took her mother no time at all to give an answer. She had been waiting for the day when she could take revenge on John the Baptizer. She had never forgiven him for having once insulted her by saying that Herod should not have married her. So back to Herod the little daughter went and repeated her mother's wish as if it were her own. "Bring me here on a platter the head of John the Baptizer!"

On hearing this, Herod looked wild-eyed at his pretty stepdaugh-

Behind its stone walls lived a lonely prisoner

ter. Behind his hard face he was wrestling with his fears. What would his guests think of him if he presented so revolting a gift to his daughter right there while they feasted? To be sure, he had been intending to put John out of the way sometime, but he was going to do it quietly. The Hermit Preacher had hundreds of followers. To have their hero killed in this horribly public way might start another riot. But what was Herod to do now that he had promised? He had carelessly given away his power. His honor as Governor was at stake. So he gave the order to an attendant, and that very night, in the midst of the reveling, the gory present was brought into the banquet hall.

In the morning, when John's friends came to the prison court to bring their teacher food, they were shocked to find the stocks empty. On learning the story of what had happened, they asked for John's body. Tenderly, with broken hearts, they bore it away and buried it beneath the desert clay near the spot where their Master had so often preached.

Soon after they sent two of their number in search of Jesus to tell him the sad news. Naturally they made their way to Capernaum and sought the home of Peter.

"May the peace of God be with you!" said Peter as he opened the door to the strangers.

"May God's peace rest upon you!" answered the two men.

"Who are you? And whom do you wish to see?" asked Peter.

"We are friends of John the Baptizer. We are seeking Jesus of Nazareth. Can you tell us where he may be?"

"Jesus is here," said Peter cordially as he showed the two strangers into the courtyard where Jesus and a few of his closest friends were sitting.

After bows and blessings all around, Jesus said: "Sit down with us, for we are eager to hear good news of your honored teacher."

"Alas, Rabbi!" said the strangers. "We have come to bring you sadness." Then they told the whole story of Salome and the feast, and how the followers of John had buried the body in the desert where their Master had once so powerfully preached.

As Jesus and his friends listened, they gasped in horror. For some moments even Jesus could not speak. One memory after another of the Hermit Preacher passed through his mind. Finally, when he was able to bring forth words, he began talking half to himself: "Was it a delicate reed that could be easily shaken in the wind that we went out into the desert to see? Were we looking for a man gorgeously clothed and sitting in a king's court? No! We went out to see a preacher — and much more than a preacher. I say unto you, no one has ever been born who was greater than John the Baptizer."

For a long while the little company sat in the moonlight, recalling experiences with the Hermit Preacher and telling stories of Herod. News of John's sudden death was like the hoisting of a danger signal.

"Herod is watching your activities, too," said one of John's disciples to Jesus. "You must be careful."

"Herod pretends he is much interested in your teachings and in your healing of the sick," said Joanna, the wife of one of Herod's men-in-waiting. "Herod wants you to come to his palace and teach him!" At this everyone laughed, except Jesus, who said: "Go and say to that fox that I shall keep on with my work as usual today and tomorrow and the third day — yes, until it is finished."

Jesus' friends looked up startled. They had never before heard their teacher speak so sarcastically.

Some days later, as evening was coming on and Jesus and his friends were walking through a certain town, one by one people began to follow after him. Each man had some question of his own to ask of the traveling teacher. Finally, when they had reached the lake shore, Jesus directed that all should sit down on the beach so that he could answer their questions and all who wished could hear.

As usual, some Pharisees were there, and the first question came from one of them. "Rabbi, when do you think the Kingdom of God will come? Shall we see the day before we die?"

Then Jesus answered them, saying: "The coming of the Kingdom of God cannot be seen with the eyes. You cannot point to it as you can point to a palace, and say 'Lo, here it is!' or 'Lo, there it is!' for the Kingdom of God is something within. It is a new life in the very heart of a man, and its beginnings are invisible.

"The Kingdom of God is not what you usually think of when you say the word 'Kingdom.' It is, rather, like a grain of mustard seed which a man takes and plants in a field. The mustard is among the smallest of seeds, and yet when it is grown it is a tree with branches in which the birds can build their nests.

"Or the Kingdom of God is like a small lump of yeast which a woman takes and hides in a large batch of meal. She waits and watches the meal as it slowly rises until finally the whole lump of dough becomes soft and light."

"That's a dream kingdom," said Judas with a nervous shake of his head. "Real kingdoms are not set up except by force. Powerful armies fight weaker armies and the strong conquer."

"Yes," said the Pharisee, "such a kingdom as Jesus thinks of is not a thing of this world at all. It belongs to heaven and to the world to come."

But Jesus answered: "God's Kingdom is different from the kingdoms of this world, but it is not just a dream and it begins here in this world. Indeed, God is ruling right now in some of your hearts. His kingdom has already come in you and in others like you who seek true righteousness."

As Jesus sat there on the shore talking, he saw a man sowing seeds on a hillside above them, and he was reminded of that day when as a boy he had first sowed seeds in a plowed field. He could never forget the thrilling moment when the great new thought took root in his mind that the Kingdom of God was a mystery like that in a living seed.

As he watched the man sowing, Jesus thought of another way to put his thoughts, and he told this story:

"Again, the Kingdom of God is like a sower who went forth to sow seeds in his field. And as he scattered the seeds from the bag at his side, some of the seeds fell by the wayside where the ground had been pressed down by passing feet. The seeds lay uncovered on top of the hard earth. Presently birds lighted upon the path and ate the seeds.

"Others of the seeds scattered by the sower fell where thorns had already taken root. The thorns grew quickly and soon choked the seeds. There was no soil left for them to feed upon.

"But others of the seeds sown fell on good and rich soil. They grew well and, when the time came, they yielded a large harvest. Some stalks bore thirty, some fifty and some one hundred times as many seeds as the sower had first planted."

When Jesus had finished with his story, he said, "So is the Kingdom of God. Its beginnings are quiet. They cannot be seen, for the thoughts of a man's heart and his love and his purpose cannot be held up to be seen; nor can you force a person to be in God's Kingdom, for a man's heart is his own. The Kingdom of God is a kingdom of spirit. It is not flesh and blood, nor lands, nor houses. And if the purpose of a man's heart is good, the way he will live and the deeds he will do will naturally become good, too.

"But growing takes time. First there is the seed, then the small plant, then the tall stalk, then a small green ear, then finally the large ear filled full with ripe wheat. And as one seed grows and produces other seeds, and these in turn produce still more seeds, so will God's Kingdom grow. In the beginning there are few. In the end there will be many.

Blessed are the gentle, the kind-hearted, for they shall inherit the earth."

For some moments no one stirred or spoke. Only the lapping of the waves on the shore could be heard. Slowly, one by one, people rose and quietly walked away. Some gathered again in small groups where they felt freer to speak their own minds. Even among those who traveled with Jesus, there were those who were keenly disappointed.

"Is this all there is to the Kingdom of God?" someone asked.

"He's not practical," said another. "I want a leader who will tell us just what we should do."

"How can you get any enthusiasm for a kingdom like that!" said a third scornfully. "Who cares for a kingdom inside a man's heart!"

"Apparently this kingdom Jesus wants has nothing to do with our national prosperity or our freedom," said Simon the Patriot. "I'm all upset. I'd been hoping Jesus might prove to be the Messiah who would free us from Rome."

"There's no fight in the man at all," said Judas. "He won't even hate our enemies. You can't get a man like that to lead a revolt."

It was a saddening experience for Jesus to find that so few people even saw the point in what he had tried to say. It was as if they were deaf. Their ears could not hear; or, hearing, they could not understand. From that time on the crowds that followed after him began to dwindle.

There were, however, many who were still enthusiastic followers. To them Jesus was the greatest man they had ever known. They stood in awe of the remarkable things he did. Had he not healed many sick people? Had he not made even the insane sound again in their minds? These people not only honored Jesus, they loved him. Just to sit near him and to watch him was the greatest privilege they could think of. Many did not bother too much if they did not understand all he said. Whatever it was, they knew it was good. It was Jesus himself they cared about.

There were others, though, who simply could not get the old hope out of their hearts. It was as if Jesus had never told them that he was not interested in trying to fight the Romans. Even James and John, the sons of Zebedee, two of Jesus' closest friends, came to him one day and said, "Master, we want you to do something for us."

"What is it you wish that I should do for you?" asked Jesus.

"Grant us that we may sit, one on your right hand and the other on your left hand, when you sit in glory on your throne."

"You do not know what you are asking," said Jesus sternly. "Instead you should be asking for courage to endure the suffering that will surely be ours. In but a few days I shall be going down to Jerusalem to attend the festival of the Passover. You know very well that the priests and the teachers there will not be friendly toward us. Some of them despise us. They may say all manner of evil against us. They may even complain of us to the Roman Governor. They may have us arrested and imprisoned. What may be ahead for us is like having to drink a cup of bitterness. If you want to follow close beside me, you must drink this cup as well as I. What I have to give you is not glory and honor and power. It is agony and weeping and crosses on the horizon."

Then Peter began to rebuke Jesus, saying, "Master, this shall never happen to you!"

"Get behind me, Peter!" said Jesus sternly. "You are like the Devil to me when you talk in this way. You are not thinking of the things of God, but of the things of men."

Then Jesus told his friends that their whole way of looking at things was wrong.

"You are thinking that the great ones are the rulers who have power to lord it over the weak," he said. "This is not so. Whoever would become great among you shall be a servant; and whoever would be first among you shall be the servant of all."

"Then don't go to Jerusalem at all," begged Judas. "Why risk your life when you could stay here in Galilee and be safe?" But Jesus would not listen.

"Whosoever would save his life shall lose it," he said solemnly, "but whosoever shall lose his life the same shall save it. For what is a man profited, if he gain the whole world, and lose his own self?"

Jesus had made his decision to go to Jerusalem and he would keep it. Worshiping in the temple at the Passover festival had been his yearly custom. He believed he had important truths to speak to the leaders in the great city. Truth was like a light in the darkness. If a man had such a light he should not hide it under a bushel basket where it could not be seen, but rather put it on a stand so as to give light to all in the house. Jesus was determined to let the light of truth shine, even though men might prefer to live in darkness.

15 The Singing Pilgrims

WITH bundles on their shoulders and money in their bags, the disciples were waiting for their Master to come so that they might start on their journey to attend the Passover festival. Since Jesus was determined to go, they had all decided to stay by him.

"Which way are we taking?" asked Peter of the others. "Will it be the short or the long way?"

"I hope it's not the long way down through the Jordan Valley," said Phillip. "It is so hot and sultry there and the wild animals frighten me at night."

"But the short way," said Judas, "is through Samaria. I simply cannot bear to sleep in the house of a Samaritan and eat food from his table."

"And besides," added Simon, "the Samaritans are dangerous. You remember the men from Capernaum who had to run for their lives out of one Samaritan village? They came near being stoned."

"This quarreling between Jews and Samaritans is foolish," broke in Thomas. "Of course, Samaritans are Jews just as much as we are."

"No, they are not," contradicted Judas. "They are half-breeds, with Babylonian blood in them."

"To be sure, some of them have a little foreign blood in them, but what of it? They believe in God, just as we do; they want to worship him with sacrifices, just as we do; and they are diligent in obeying the law. Why should we quarrel with them?"

"Well," said James, "the Samaritans are proud of their little temple on Mount Gerizim, but in their hearts they are angry at us for being so exclusive."

"I suppose," said Judas a bit scornfully, "if we followed Jesus' teaching we would let any foreigner who wanted to do so worship in our temple."

"Yes," said John, half wondering if he meant what he was going to say, "I suppose Jesus would say to take down that sign from the temple wall. You know, the one I mean, beside the Beautiful Gate at the entrance to the Women's Court. The way it reads now is: 'Any foreigner who enters beyond this wall into the temple does so at the risk of his life.' But I suppose Jesus would have it read: 'Welcome, foreigners from all the nations. Come and worship with us. The Lord our God is one God!'" Some half laughed at John when he said this. The idea seemed so absurd. Others thought to themselves, "If that day ever came, it would really be the Kingdom of God."

"Well, here is Jesus coming now," said Peter. "Let us take the road he prefers."

"Which will it be, Master?" Peter asked. "The long way or the short way?"

"Let us go down through Samaria," Jesus answered. "I like to use every opportunity we have to be friendly with the Samaritans."

So the little pilgrim band set forth on its long walk southward toward the great city. It was one of those pleasant days in spring when the air is heavy with the scent of flowers. Red and yellow anemones colored the hillsides and the trees were delicate with small leaves. Except for a couple of hours of rest at noontime, the travelers walked all day long. As evening drew near, their feet were weary. On seeing a village in the distance, Jesus said to James and John, "Go into yonder village and find rooms where we may rest for the night."

So the two men walked ahead. On entering the village, they found a small inn. Knocking at the door, they bowed courteously to the owner and asked if they might hire a sleeping place for the night.

"Who are you?" asked the Samaritan brusquely. "And where are you going?"

"We are Galilean pilgrims on our way to the Passover at Jerusalem."

"Away with you! We will have no Jews sleeping in our town." And he slammed the door in their faces.

Hot with anger, James and John turned and ran back quickly to Jesus to tell of the abusive way in which they had been treated.

"Master," they pleaded, "go to the man yourself and speak to him. He may respect you. If he does not, you should have him punished. This is a terrible insult. You remember how Elijah called on God to send down fire from heaven and burn up his enemies? You should do the same. You are as great as Elijah."

But Jesus rebuked the two men for their anger. "You do not realize the kind of spirit you have within you. Have you forgotten how we Jews have been sinning against these Samaritans, lo, these hundreds of years? Let him that has no sin in his heart be the first one to call down fire upon them."

For a moment Jesus waited to see what his friends would do, but not one of them had anything more to say.

So, with Jesus and Peter leading the way, the travelers turned back and found a valley road leading down to the Jordan. They would go to Jerusalem the long way.

Finally Peter was the first to speak. "I never knew before how it feels to be cast out and hated. At first I was as angry as James and John."

"But now?" asked Jesus.

"But now," said Peter, "I think I can honestly pray the prayer you once taught us."

"And what was that," asked Jesus.

"Our Father who art in heaven,

"Forgive us our sins as we forgive those who have sinned against us."

.   .   .   .

Two days later, Jesus and his little band of followers were nearing Jerusalem. They had just left Jericho, the beautiful city of palms and flowers, and were now on the last twenty miles of their long pilgrimage. The road was dusty, hot and steep. There were no trees to shade the path and no green to rest the eyes. But by mid-afternoon the pilgrims reached the village of Bethany at the back of the Mount of Olives. There they found grassy fields and olive orchards and plentiful fig trees and fresh spring water to drink. And best of all was the glad welcome in the home of their good friends, Mary and Martha and Lazarus. There the pilgrims found many others on their way to Jerusalem. Some had arrived earlier, while others came up the road after the evening meal. Although every family welcomed into their homes as many strangers as they could make comfortable, yet hundreds had to set up camp

The road was dusty,
hot and steep

on the slopes outside the town and sleep in the moonlight. It was a relief that the next day was the Sabbath, for some had been on their way for weeks. All were glad for a good reason to rest for a day.

Early on the first day of the week after the Sabbath, the path up the Mount of Olives began again to swarm with travelers. It was a stirring sight to watch them pass by — men, women and children, each carrying some bundle. Here and there was a donkey loaded with camping supplies, or someone leading a sheep or goat or lamb to be sacrificed during the festival.

When Jesus and his little band joined the procession, they began discovering people who knew them. Some of them had heard Jesus speak in their synagogues. Signals were waved back and forth among friends to spread the news that Jesus was in the company.

"With Jesus at the Passover," they said, "something important will surely happen. Does not something important always happen where Jesus is?"

Finally the exciting moment came when the pilgrims reached a lookout on the top of the mountain, where they could see over the Kedron Valley to the west and feast their eyes on the city of their dreams. Some had never before seen the Holy City. To look on it now was the dream of a lifetime come true. It was almost as if they could reach out their hands and touch the white walls of the great, massive temple. They could look down into its open courts — rising one above the other in terraces. They could even see the crowds of people like toy figures moving about in the great outer court. Plainer than all else was the column of black smoke rising from the altar, for the morning sacrifice for all the people was still burning.

Inspired by this impressive sight, someone among the pilgrims started to sing. Immediately others picked up the chorus. "Hosanna! Hosanna! Glory to God in the highest!" Over and over they sang the words:

Enter into his gates with thanksgiving,
And into his courts with praise.
Serve the Lord with gladness;
Come before his presence with singing.
Blessed is he that cometh in the name of the Lord!

Who could help but sing when standing on such a lookout? All the pilgrims had come in the name of the Lord to worship in this Holy Temple. And now the great day had come. Everyone felt blessed and wanted to linger awhile.

But before long, one group after another left the lookout and started down the mountain into the valley. Presently a friend offered Jesus a donkey. "It is not needed by my family," he said. "It's bundles can be easily transferred to another beast." With some hesitation, Jesus yielded to the man's wish and, to the great delight of his many friends, he rode the donkey. So the procession moved along down into the valley and up the road beside the northern walls of the city. Some gathered flowers growing near the path and threw them at Jesus, laughing as they did so. Others picked off branches from nearby bushes and waved them, shouting his name. Some even took off their cloaks and laid them across the path so that Jesus and his donkey would walk over them. Again the crowds burst into song:

Hosanna! Hosanna!
Enter into his gates with thanksgiving;
And into his courts with praise.
Blessed is he that cometh in the name of the Lord.

But Jesus himself was not happy over the shouting and singing now that he realized that part of the excitement was on his account. It was dangerous for these people to be hoping for some great thing from him at the festival. At such a time as the Passover, the people were so easily excited. The whole festival reminded them of their need for freedom. Any shouting patriot could enlist the crowds at such a time as this. But to start a rebellion against Rome in this fashion would be the greatest folly.

As Jesus was thinking these thoughts he looked up and saw high on the Tower of Antonia armored soldiers watching and listening. If only they could understand, they would know that Jesus was not the least bit interested in stirring up the people against them. His one great desire was to help his people to find another kind of freedom — a freedom no tyrant could ever destroy.

A Pharisee walking alongside Jesus, and noticing his anxious face, asked: "Master, why don't you rebuke your followers and command them to be quiet?"

"If I commanded the people not to sing, the stones in the road would have to sing for them. Passover pilgrims entering Jerusalem are always singing."

But Jesus' heart was not singing. Those near him saw that instead he was weeping. He cried out as if calling to the men and women walking about on top of the city walls: "Oh, Jerusalem! Jerusalem! If only you understood the things that belong with peace; but, alas, these are hidden from your eyes."

As the singing procession moved on through the great gate in the city wall and into a narrow, crowded street, passers-by stared with curiosity. "Who is this?" they asked, "that is so popular?" "It is Jesus, the preacher from Nazareth." But very soon the procession became lost among the crowds and scattered. Relieved, Jesus stepped down from his donkey, gave it back to his friend, and walked along with the crowds. Presently he was but one among thousands thronging the great outer court of the temple.

Although it was still five days until the great day of the Passover supper, thousands of pilgrims were already in the city, each bent on making some personal sacrifice in the temple and each bringing some personal gift as a token of thanksgiving.

Officers of the temple stood about here and there in the great court to direct the crowds and to answer questions.

"What kind of animal should I buy? I must confess my sins."

"Where may I find the priest who will wash me clean with water, because I have eaten food prepared by foreigners?"

"Where shall I take these gifts — this bottle of wine and this bag of meal, which we have brought from our own vineyard and field?"

"Where shall I leave this sheep until my turn comes at the altar?"

There was much coming and going, pushing and worrying. Mothers tried to hold on to their children, and husbands tried to keep in touch with their wives.

Jesus and his companions soon edged their way through the crowds and up the fourteen steps leading to the Beautiful Gate of brass and on into the Court of the Women. There they found white-robed priests standing behind a row of large silver bowls, ready to receive the gifts of the worshipers. Into the first of these bowls, Jesus and his companions, one by one, dropped their half-shekels — the temple tax required of every Jew. Then each, according to his own desire, dropped other coins in other bowls. These were gifts of their own choosing — freewill offerings. Jesus put his into the bowl marked "for the poor."

Then, when all had given their gifts, they sat down on benches arranged along the wall where they might rest awhile. On the steps leading to the next higher court, a white-gowned choir was singing, while men with harps and flutes and cymbals accompanied it. Now and again a priest would lead the worshipers in saying prayers.

As Jesus and his followers sat thus in the Court of the Women, a continual line of worshipers passed before them. In addition to the temple tax, they brought gifts of many kinds. Some brought jewels or pieces of silver or precious stones and gave them to the priests standing beside the bowls.

Two worshipers who came to the court that day were unforgettable. The first was a tall, richly dressed man, in a purple gown with a long, tasseled shawl hanging about his head and shoulders. As he stood proudly before one of the bowls, he lifted a bag full of coins high above the bowl and, turning it upside down, he let the coins fall clanging one by one into the silver bowl as if he wished all those about him to know how much money he was giving.

The next to pass by was a frail old woman, leaning on a cane. She was dressed in a dull sackcloth gown with a veil hanging over her shoulders, partly covering her face. She seemed to see no one as she hobbled to the bowl and dropped in two of the smallest coins.

"It was just a farthing!" whispered Peter.

"Yes," Jesus replied. "Yet this poor widow has cast into the bowl more than all the others we have seen, for these others have been giving out of their riches, but she in her poverty has put in all she had — even all her living."

At the close of the day, as Jesus and his disciples walked back to the Mount of Olives and to Bethany, some of them were excited and full of talk. How important and happy they had felt when the pilgrims on the road shouted and sang and threw their flowers and waved branches! Then how small and inconspicuous they had felt, wandering about the immense temple court where in all the sea of faces about them they recognized only a few now and then!

16 "A Den of Robbers"

THE following morning, Jesus and his disciples went again to the temple. Jesus was hoping that he might have an opportunity to sit down in one of the cloisters on the edge of the great outer court and teach. Some would surely gather about him to hear and to ask questions.

But when he reached the temple court, he found it crammed with pilgrims, even more so than the day before. He could not say how many thousands there were, but the mass of people extended from one end of the court to the other as far as his eyes could see. Jesus tried to work his way through the crowd to the eastern side of the open court and around the temple building toward the north end. He was hoping to find some quieter spot among the pillars. But there he was met by a flock of bleating sheep, each being led by the man who had bought it in the temple market just outside the walls. Temple officials were standing about like policemen directing the men with animals to the gate leading into the place of sacrifice.

On finding no place for quiet, Jesus worked his way through the crowds along the eastern and southern cloisters. There he found other temple officials, standing behind tables and in booths, calling out the things they had for sale — bags of meal, bottles of wine, spices, oils, incense, everything handy for any kind of sacrifice.

For a long while Jesus watched and listened as the people came to buy. He was surprised to find the prices so much higher than in the markets outside. Some refused to pay. Others complained angrily, but to no effect. "How the money is rolling in to the temple treasury!" thought Jesus.

At the tables of the money-changers, the crowds were so thick that people had to stand waiting even to get close enough to the tables to do their business. Jews from foreign lands, bringing foreign money, wished to have it changed for Judean money. There were coins from Greece, and Egypt, from Babylonia and Rome—indeed from everywhere in the world, it seemed. The merchants were charging high fees for their services. Such charges were making the money-changers rich, but travelers, who had already spent so much just to attend the festival, were being cheated. Jesus' heart burned with anger as he watched the hard faces of the men behind the counters.

Turning away indignantly, he said to the disciples who had been following him about: "This temple court is a den of robbers!"

Next, he came upon tables piled high with cages filled with doves. Barefooted women stood about. Their garments were soiled from work in the fields and their faces wrinkled and brown with the sun and winds. There were shepherds, too, camel drivers, tanners, beggars — the city's poor — who could not afford to buy animals for sacrifices. Half afraid that they would not have enough money, they were asking the prices of the doves.

"You've given only a quarter of a shekel, woman," said the merchant at the table. "The price of this dove is a half-shekel."

Jesus saw the woman leave the booth sobbing, with a frightened child tugging at her garments. He went immediately over to the merchant and talked with him directly.

"A quarter of a shekel is surely a fair price," said Jesus. "You must not forget for whom the doves have been provided."

"But our doves are all perfect ones," insisted the merchant. "Every single one has been examined and passed by one of the priests."

But Jesus answered: "By your high prices, you are robbing the poor of the chance to bring any offerings at all to God's altar." The merchant merely shrugged his shoulders and turned to another customer.

Jesus turned and took the woman in one hand and the young child in the other, and walked away. "Do not be discouraged," he said to her. "Our Father in heaven knows what you have need of before you ask him. He is more ready to give good gifts to you than you are to give food to this child of yours. Pray to him in the secret of your own heart. He will understand why you have not brought an offering to the temple."

All the while as Jesus was talking, the little child was watching him, and Jesus was looking down with a tender smile on the child's upturned face. He could not understand the words Jesus was saying, but the child's tears disappeared as dewdrops vanish in the sunlight. Presently Jesus bade the mother and child good by and the two walked off quietly hand in hand.

But Jesus stayed on. With a heavy heart he walked about through the crowds, and in the indignant faces of those about him he saw mirrowed his own sense of injustice. Finally he could no longer hold back his anger. It was right to be angry, he thought to himself. These hardhearted, selfish men will be changed only by force.

He turned and walked back to the men who were selling doves. "Take your cages out of the temple!" he commanded. "This is a sacred place. The Scripture says that God's house shall be called a House of Prayer for all the nations, but you have made it a den of robbers."

But the men paid no attention or answered back with harsh words. Then Jesus took hold of one of the cages, and opened the wicker gate. Away flew the doves! Some of his followers near by picked up other cages and opened their gates, also. Soon all the cages had been emptied and the doves were flying about under the cloister roof and out and up into the open sky.

In despair the merchants tried to hold on to their cages, but the men were helpless. The people shouted and clapped their hands. "Thieves and robbers you all are!" they cried. "Away with you!"

Next Jesus walked to the corner of the cloisters where the money-changers sat with their piles of coins before them. He spoke to them in the same manner in which he had spoken to the sellers of doves. They, too, responded defiantly. "Who are you to tell us what we ought to do?" they cried. "The High Priest has given us our permit. Are you greater than he?" In a flash someone in the

"Take your cages out of the temple!"

crowd upset one of the tables so that the coins went rolling in all directions over the stone pavement. Quickly another table was tipped over and another. Almost before the merchants had time to grasp what was happening, the people were scrambling about gathering up whatever coins they could and tucking them away in their bags. Cheers mingled with curses and the laughter of the crowds, with the banging of the tables on the stone pavements as the merchants angrily left the court.

Roman soldiers from the Castle were pacing back and forth on the roof above the cloisters overlooking the courts. They heard the clatter and cheering, and looked down in amazement on the confusion. But since they saw no fighting with swords and no bloodshed, they did nothing. In fact they were a bit amused at what seemed to them an undignified affair.

Three of the white-robed priests busy in the inner courts, on hearing the noise of the commotion, left their work and came out to see what was happening. As they stood at the top of the steps in the Beautiful Gateway they were amazed at the shouting, scrambling crowds in the wide court below. Was this another bloody riot on their hands? Should they call upon the Roman soldiers to quiet the crowds? What was the excitement all about, anyway? Who had stirred up the people to such boldness? Had they lost all respect for the temple authorities? Again and again, the priests shouted for quiet, but few heard their threats, and fewer still even noticed their presence at the top of the steps.

After what seemed a very long time, the confusion began to lessen. Jesus pushed his way forward through the throng. He stood at the foot of the steps and looked up at the three bewildered priests. Then turning, he faced the multitude and called, "It is written." The people recognized the voice. They called to one another for quiet. "It is written," Jesus called again. "My house shall be called a House of Prayer for all the nations, but our priests have made it a den of robbers!"

Facing the priests once more, Jesus spoke directly to them. "You, priests of the Lord, have brought marketing into these holy courts, not to serve the worshipers but to bring wealth to yourselves. By your unfair prices, you have taken food from the mouths of orphans. You have been stealing from widows to keep these ceremonies going. God desires mercy more than sacrifices, but you desire sacrifices more than mercy."

Wild shouts rose from the people who thronged about him. "The rabbi is right! Praise the Lord!"

The priests were maddened by the insult, yet they did not dare to fight the mob. Bewildered, they could make no answer. Proudly they turned around and walked back to the inner courts.

As the day wore on, the tumult became less violent. The crowds grew smaller. Over in a cloister Jesus at last found a place where he could sit on a little platform against one of the giant pillars. For a long while, people squatted around him listening quietly to his words and asking him questions.

At last the evening hour came. The trumpeter, standing on the pinnacle of the temple, blew his silver trumpet three times to announce the moment of sunset. The evening sacrifice of an ox was being offered for all the people. As Jesus and his disciples left the holy place, a thick column of smoke curled upward from the stone altar. Once more the little company returned to the Mount of Olives and spent the night in Bethany with their friends, Mary and Martha.

That evening, news of the excitement in the temple spread like wildfire through the entire city. The Roman guards carried word of the riot to Pilate, the Governor, as he sat at dinner in his palace. "So bold a man as this Jesus of Nazareth is dangerous," said Pilate. "He must be watched. If another riot occurs, arrest him."

Many of Jesus' own followers who had known him for a long time were surprised at the sudden change they thought they saw in him. They said: "Always before, Jesus has refused to fight. 'Resist not evil. Love your enemies.' These were his very words. But today he was a fighter himself — not with a sword, to be sure, but with the whip of his tongue."

"He's a real prophet!" said others. "Like Amos and Jeremiah and John the Baptizer."

"The rule and power of the priests seems to Jesus to be worse than the rule and power of Rome. If only he would talk back to Pilate with the same boldness with which he talked today to the priests, he might free us even yet."

"No, you can't get Jesus to do that," said one of the Pharisees. "He says that we must seek righteousness first, and he is right. He means righteousness for ourselves in our own living with one another and with God. Then all these other things will be added unto us some day."

"I agree with Jesus entirely," said another Pharisee. "If every Jew would obey the laws of God faithfully, we could trust God to free us from the Romans."

Such discussions went on long into the night.

To the High Priest and to his many assistants in the temple, what had happened seemed serious indeed. These priests were responsible for all the trading in the temple, and as a result, the families of the higher ranking priests had become very rich.

The chief priests were agreed that Jesus was a dangerous man. "We must find a way to get rid of him," they said. "If we do not, he will destroy the whole religious life of our people. He might as well pull the whole temple down as to go on doing what he did today. Pilgrims will cease coming to worship in God's holy temple. We shall be disgraced before the people, and our means of livelihood will be destroyed."

So the priests began plotting how they might arrest Jesus without stirring up the anger of the crowds against themselves. Even some of the people, who the day before had shouted the praises of this teacher from Galilee, were now wondering whether or not they had better pin their hopes on him any longer. Was Jesus a bad Jew after all? Was he really trying to destroy the religion of their fathers? It was hard for most of them to believe that he was; but if the priests thought so, what could the ordinary person say?

17 Secret Plottings

THE next morning, Jesus and his disciples went again to the temple as if nothing had happened. Although the great outer court was thronged with pilgrims as on the day before, there was less confusion and noise. The money-changers and those who sold articles needed in the sacrifices worked more quietly, and the dove sellers had but a few cages full of birds.

Here and there in the cloisters, teachers sat with groups of students around them. For most of the day Jesus was the center of such a group. A Pharisee or two was usually there and some priest off duty was sure to be present listening, hoping to catch Jesus in a rash remark which might be used against him if he were arrested and brought before the Governor.

Some of the questions put to Jesus were these: By whose power did you act yesterday when you dared to criticize the way the priests manage the temple? Who do you think the Messiah will be — a plain man like yourself, or someone of royal blood? And what do you think — should we pay taxes to the Emperor? On being asked this last question, Jesus asked for a coin. Holding it up so that all might see, he said, "Whose picture is stamped on this coin?" And when the answer was given that it was the Roman Emperor's picture, Jesus said, "Then give to Caesar the things that are Caesar's and to God the things that are God's."

"A very clever answer!" whispered one priest to another. "It's hard to make a rebel out of him!"

A certain teacher, hearing that Jesus had cleverly put his questioners to silence in this way, decided he would try to see if he could catch Jesus in a mistake.

Standing up before him, the man said, "Master, which is the first and greatest commandment?"

Jesus answered, "You also are a teacher of the Law. How do you yourself understand what is written?"

And the man said: "The first commandment is, 'Thou shalt love the Lord thy God with all thy heart, and with all thy soul, and with all thy mind, and with all thy strength.' The second is this, 'Thou shalt love thy neighbor as thyself.' There is none other commandment greater than these. To obey these is much more important than all the burnt offerings and sacrifices made in this temple."

Pleased at hearing the man speak in this way, Jesus said: "You have answered rightly. This do and you shall live."

But the man, wishing to defend himself, asked: "The difficulty about this second law is to know who my neighbor is. It's quite impossible to include everybody."

On hearing this second question Jesus realized that the man was probably thinking of foreigners or Samaritans. Evidently he did not think these people should be treated as neighbors. Jesus was reminded of what he and his disciples had experienced as they were coming down to Jerusalem through Samaria, and then Jesus told this story.

"Once upon a time," Jesus began, "a certain merchant was traveling from Jerusalem to Jericho. It is a lonely and dangerous journey, as you well know, down through the steep and barren hills. Suddenly, at a turn in the road, the merchant was held up by a band of robbers who stripped off his clothes, stole all his merchandise and left him lying by the roadside in the hot sun, half naked and half dead.

"After a long while another traveler chanced to come by on the road. He was a priest who, having completed his period of duty at the temple, was going back to his home for a rest. On coming to the spot, he noticed a half-naked man lying by the roadside, but he did not go over to see if the man were merely sleeping or if he were in trouble. Instead the priest passed by on the other side of the road.

"After another long wait, a second traveler came along. He was a singer in one of the temple choirs. When he came to the spot, he also noticed the man lying beside the road, but he also passed him by.

"Finally, a certain Samaritan merchant came by, leading a donkey loaded with merchandise. He was planning to sell his goods in Jericho where many foreigners lived who were willing to have dealings with the Samaritans.

"When this Samaritan saw the man lying half naked beside the road, he stepped over beside him to find out what was the matter. When he saw the man's bleeding face and back, the Samaritan felt pity for the wounded man and took a camel-skin bottle hanging from his girdle and poured some of the oil in it over the wounds. Then he bound them up with a piece of cloth that he found in his bag of merchandise.

"The Samaritan then unloaded his own donkey and lifted the helpless man up on the donkey's back. He picked up his bundles of merchandise, threw them over his own shoulders and, carefully leading the donkey with the wounded man on its back, he went on his way.

So together they traveled on until they came to an inn. There the Samaritan secured a room for the night, spread his own sleeping mat on the floor, and laid the injured man down to rest.

All through the night, the Samaritan slept beside the man and waited on him whenever he needed help.

"When morning came, since the wounded man was better and was able to move about a little, the Samaritan bade him good-by and started on his way. But, before leaving, he paid the keeper of the inn for lodging for two and told him that he wished the man to stay there as long as he needed to do so. 'Take care of him,' the Samaritan said, 'and whatever you spend more than I have given you, I will repay you when I come back again from Jericho.'"

After finishing the story, Jesus turned to the teacher who had asked the question and put another one to him. He said: "Which of these three men, the priest or the choir singer or the Samaritan, proved to be neighbor to the man who had been held up by robbers?"

The teacher answered without hesitation, "The man who showed mercy on him." What else could he say? The answer was clear. But Jesus' question of the man was not the same as the

With the wounded man on the donkey's back,
he went on his way

question he had asked of Jesus. The man was puzzled. He had failed to start the argument he wanted. But he was afraid to ask another question. Soon he slipped away from the little crowd that sat around Jesus. Several others followed him.

Presently a small group of Jesus' critics met in another part of the temple court. "He was not very complimentary to priests and temple officers, was he? But we'll get even with him some day," said one.

"If a man stopped to help every beggar he saw by the roadside, he'd get nowhere," another replied.

"After all, we have to be practical," added a third. "This Jesus is a dreamer. He thinks we can have a perfect world."

From that time on none of the priests tried to catch Jesus by asking him questions.

. . . .

At the close of the day, as Jesus and his disciples were walking across the great outer court to leave the temple, some of them remarked about the high stone pillars in the cloisters.

"Think of it!" said one. "This pillar must be twenty feet high, and it is all one single stone!"

"And how could workmen ever carry such stones as these up to the top of this high place and set them up?" asked a second.

"You have to respect Herod the Great for one thing," said Peter. "He helped us rebuild our temple. Just think of it! This temple was begun fifty years ago and it is not yet finished."

"You have spoken truly," said James. "Such a magnificent building as this will stand forever."

"It is better not to boast," said Jesus. "This temple has twice before been destroyed. If the Romans are roused to anger against us, they will have no respect for this holy place."

"Master," asked Judas, "what do you think the Romans might do?"

"They would not leave one stone lying on another."

"May God forbid!" cried Judas. "If our temple is destroyed, all our glory as a nation will be gone, for we would no longer be able to worship God according to the Law."

"No, Judas, you are wrong," said Jesus in reply. "Perhaps then we would have the eyes to see a greater temple — one not made with hands — as everlasting as the skies and the hills. That temple we can build at any spot where there is air and sky and earth. Anywhere may be a House of Prayer for those who worship in spirit and in truth. Such worshipers our Father desires."

But Judas, too shocked to think on Jesus' words, turned and walked away. He tried to hide himself in the shadow of one of the pillars. Presently two strangers passed near him, unaware of his presence. They were talking in low tones.

"This man thinks he can destroy the temple. He claims he can build an even greater one to take its place. Is this not so?"

"Those were his very words," said the other. "What this man did yesterday is just the beginning of what he intends to do."

"I must report this at once to the High Priest."

"And I must see that Pilate is told," said the other.

On overhearing this conversation, Judas became thoroughly frightened. He knew very well that Jesus had never said those words. Evidently a Roman spy had been following Jesus, and agents of the priests had been helping to gather evidence against him. What could Judas do? Wasn't Jesus himself to blame? How could a loyal Jewish patriot speak so calmly about destroying the holy temple? To follow such a leader would be to betray his own country. The longer Judas pondered the clearer the issue seemed: it was either his country or his friend. Judas could no longer be loyal to both, and trying to choose tore his heart in two.

Nervously he paced back and forth in the shadows. The other disciples had forgotten him. With Jesus they had left the temple and were already on their way back to Bethany. Judas knew not whether minutes passed or hours.

In the meantime, the High Priest and several of his associates were talking together in the High Priest's private room.

"That Galilean disturber from Nazareth," said one, "has had the boldness to teach in the temple all day long. One of our spies reports that he heard the man say he would destroy our holy temple and in its place another great temple would be put up without the help of any human hands!"

"What!" shouted the High Priest. "Have we uncovered a Galilean plot to destroy the temple?" Every one gasped in horror at the thought.

"Pontius Pilate must be told at once," continued the High Priest, "lest he blame us for the serious riots which may occur. We must again impress upon our governor how very popular this preacher is with thousands of the pilgrims. Pilate must know that the man has friends even among our most highly respected rabbis. Some are even asking, 'Could the Messiah be more wonderful than this leader?' "

Heads nodded and murmurs of approval came from every priest in the circle. Some used abusive language against Jesus. The welfare of the nation was at stake. Let this preacher continue to speak publicly and the Jewish people would lose their most cherished liberty. They would no longer be allowed to worship in the holy temple.

While this important meeting was going on, the desperate Judas in the court outside made his fateful choice. Nervously he walked towards the High Priest's room, vaguely hoping he might meet someone coming out. He knew now that their spies had been following Jesus. Perhaps Judas might talk with one of them.

Presently he met a Roman guard pacing his beat. Judas began talking with him, and soon was telling just what he had been doing and why. "Do you realize," said Judas, "what a dangerous leader this Galilean teacher is?"

"We certainly do," said the guard. "We've been watching

him all day and the priests even now are scheming how to arrest him without stirring up the anger of the crowds who almost worship him."

As a result, strange things began to happen. The Roman guard arranged for Judas to speak with one of the priests. Soon Judas found himself standing before the august circle of priests and answering their questions. Could he tell them where they might find Jesus alone or with but a few friends?

Judas was sure he knew exactly where they might find Jesus sooner or later. It was in a certain garden on the hillside near the path to Bethany. "If he's not there tonight, he will be tomorrow night. I will follow him from now on, and will let you know promptly when I'm certain he will be in the garden. Be prepared to act quickly when I send you word."

As Judas bowed himself out of the room, one of the priests arose from his seat; and, without saying anything, placed some coins in Judas' hand.

Absent-mindedly Judas took the money and walked from the room. Scarcely knowing where he was going, he wandered in a daze out through the temple gate. He strolled aimlessly through one dark street after another until he was finally outside the city wall. As he walked along the open path under the twilight sky, his mind began slowly to clear.

He looked down at his closed hand, and opened it to see what he had been carrying. He counted ten, twenty, thirty pieces of silver. Could it be that he had taken a bribe for what he had done? He thought he had acted as a patriot. He thought he had risked his life for the sake of his country. Could it be he had been hired to spy? As Judas stared at the money in his hand, a feeling of dreadful shame bore down upon him like a heavy weight. He half wanted to throw the money away.

Instead he ran down the path into the Kedron valley as if to prove that he was still strong. He trudged up the Mount of Olives and over to Bethany. There he found Jesus and the other disciples sitting about an open fire talking and singing. Judas tried to act as if nothing had happened to him, but his secret kept pulling his words back whenever he tried to talk. As the little company separated for the night, Peter said: "Judas, you have been unusually quiet this evening. What is the matter?" But that was all.

18 The Shadow of Death

AND now the morning of the great day of the festival had come. In the evening each Jewish family would eat the Passover supper with gladness and singing. Ever since Jesus and his twelve disciples had put in their lot together, this yearly Passover supper had been a time of special happiness.

"Master," asked Peter, "where would you like us to make ready for the supper?"

"I've made an arrangement with one of my friends in the city," Jesus replied. "He has a large upstairs room which he says he would be happy to have us use."

"Where is the house?" asked Peter.

"Each morning regularly my friend sends his servant to the spring near the Water Gate. If you go at once, you will meet the man coming back from there with a jar of water on his head; follow him until he turns into his house. Then knock at the door and say to the master of the house: 'Our Teacher wishes us to ask where the guest room is in which he may eat the Passover supper with his disciples.' Then he will show you a large upper room, furnished and ready. There you may complete the plans for our supper."

So Peter and John went up to Jerusalem, while Jesus and the other disciples stayed quietly in Bethany. The two disciples found everything just as Jesus had said. A long, low table was there with benches around it. On a stand against the wall were a large jar filled with water, and two clay basins and two pitchers and towels ready for the washing of feet and hands.

Peter and John were pleased with what they found and started off to the market to buy the supplies needed for the supper — plenty of bitter herbs and round flat loaves of unleavened bread, reminders of the bitter years of slavery in Egypt; also dates, raisins, apples, nuts, spices and wine. Bringing these articles back to the house, the disciples found several of the women already there waiting to prepare the supper.

Again Peter and John set out for another market where lambs for the evening sacrifice were for sale. There the men picked out as perfect a one-year-old lamb as they could find and, buying it, they led it up to the temple mount and into the great open court. There they waited their turn among thousands of other pilgrims and among thousands of young lambs which, like their own, would soon be sacrified. When Peter and John's turn came, they led their lamb up into the higher court, and, as it was killed, a priest stood by with a silver bowl to gather its blood and to pour it out on the great stone altar.

All the while the white-robed choir sang hymns of praise, or a priest led the people in prayer. As the two men watched and listened, they felt that the priests through their prayers and songs were bringing God's blessing upon their offering.

Returning to the house where the supper was to be eaten, Peter and John built a fire in the open courtyard behind the house, and hung the lamb on a spit to roast over the fire. By evening, when the trumpeter on the temple pinnacle blew his silver trumpet to announce the hour of sunset, Jesus and his disciples were gathering in the upstairs room eager to begin the celebration.

As the men entered they found the room gayly lighted with lamps hanging from the ceiling. A long, low table with benches and stools arranged about it made them feel welcome. In the center of the table was a platter piled high with round flat loaves of bread. On one side was a cruse of wine and on the other a bowl of raisins and figs. Although the women were still busy with a few last things, one was there by the door with a basin in one hand and a pitcher of water in the other. As each man held his hands over the basin, she poured water over them that his hands might be properly washed before the meal.

But there was no other woman who could be spared from the supper preparations to wash the men's feet and on such a special occasion as this surely their dusty feet should be washed. Since this was always a servant's or a wife's job, none of the men even thought of the possibility of offering to do so menial a task. Apparently the company would sit down with dusty feet to eat this Passover supper. "It probably doesn't matter," some thought. "Jesus is not particular about such forms."

So the men stood about talking. Some began to speculate quietly on where they were to be seated and to scheme so that they might have the seats of honor nearest their teacher. Before long Jesus felt an unfriendliness spreading like a fog through the room. He saw pride and jealousy behind whispered words and watchful eyes. What could he do?

It did not take Jesus long to decide. He realized that his friends would be shocked, but they needed to be awakened into a new understanding.

Without a word of explanation, Jesus laid aside his outer cloak and wrapped a towel around his waist. Finding a large earthen basin, he set it on the floor before one of his friends, and when he had filled it with water, he began to wash the man's feet and to wipe them with the towel.

Each man in turn objected strongly to Jesus' doing such com-

"But I am your servant also."

mon and dirty work, but Jesus insisted that he wanted to do it. Peter refused absolutely when his turn came. "You shall never wash my feet," he said positively.

"If I do not wash you, then you are not one of my friends," said Jesus jokingly.

At once Peter answered, "Master, wash then not only my feet but also my hands and my head." Jesus laughed but he liked Peter for saying this.

144

When Jesus had finished washing the feet of all the men, he again put on his cloak and they all sat down around the table. "Do you know why I did this?" he asked. "You call me Teacher or Master, and you say, 'Of course, that is what you are.' But I am your servant also. If such work is not too common for me, it is not too common for you. The disciple is not above his Teacher. Which is greater, he that sits at the table or he that serves the meal? Do you not usually say, he that sits at the table? But I say to you it is he that serves the meal."

Jesus then led his friends in prayer; after the prayer he filled a large cup with wine and, taking a sip, he passed it around, asking each one to drink of it. So the supper began. There was much ceremony throughout the whole meal, singing, repeating Psalms from the Bible, many prayers and also much pleasant conversation. Occasionally the men were even jolly. But as the hours passed and it grew late, Jesus became less gay. He began to talk solemnly as if he felt some danger looming ahead like a great shadow before them. He said he felt that this might perhaps be the last Passover supper he would ever celebrate with them on earth. He tried to comfort his disciples as if he were going to leave them. He, too, needed comfort from them. He needed the comfort of knowing they understood. "Let not your hearts be troubled, neither let them be fearful," he said, partly to them and partly to himself. "God knows what we have need of before we ask him."

It was about midnight, after they had sung a hymn, when they all went away together, down the stairs, and out into the quiet night. Almost without saying a word, they passed out through the city gate and down across the Kedron Valley and up the slopes of the Mount of Olives. All were there except Judas. Earlier, before the meal was finished, he had slipped quietly out of the room. He was now on his way to the house of the High Priest to let the rulers of the temple know that the time had come.

After climbing a short way up the mountain, Jesus and his disciples came to a garden of olive trees, called by its owner Gethsemane. Since the garden belonged to a long-time friend, Jesus felt free to go in. Opening the gate in the wall that surrounded the garden, he and his companions entered. When they had walked a little way up into the garden, Jesus said to his disciples, "My soul is sorrowful. I wish to be alone. Sit here and rest and watch that no one comes to disturb us. I shall go farther up the hillside."

So the disciples sat down on the grass together while Jesus went on for a distance, about as far as a man can throw a stone, and there he sat down alone at the foot of an olive tree. He felt he must have the peace of the moonlight and the quiet of being alone in the darkness in order to think and to pray. His heart was heavy with trouble. He felt as though all he had lived for was about to come to nothing. Even his closest friends seemed to understand so little. And so many of the men who were in power hated him for trying to change their customs. It was hard to accept the bitterness of this disappointment. Finally, he gathered all that was in him into one great resolve, and he kneeled down and prayed: "O Father, all things are possible to thee. If thou art willing, save me from being arrested and killed. Let this bitter cup pass from me. But if it cannot be, may thy will be done."

When Jesus had made this resolve and had spoken it to God, he felt strengthened. He could accept whatever came. He could drink the bitter cup, for he believed God would not desert him now.

Rising from his knees, Jesus walked back down the hill to where he had left his disciples to wait and to watch. Not realizing how long he had been gone, Jesus was surprised to find them all asleep, but he wakened them saying, "Never mind. The spirit indeed is willing but the body is weak."

Even while Jesus was talking with his disciples and before they were fully awake, Judas suddenly appeared coming up the path; behind him was a company of officers from the temple, carrying swords and cudgels and lighted lanterns. Running up to Jesus, Judas put his arms around him and kissed him, saying, "Hail, Rabbi!"

It was so quickly done, Jesus was dazed. It took him a moment to believe it could be true. Judas, his intimate friend, his companion at the supper table that very evening — Judas had kissed him! His greeting seemed so hearty and yet at his back in the darkness — soldiers, with swords and cudgels!

"Have you come with swords and cudgels to seize me as if I were a robber?" asked Jesus. "I have been sitting daily in the temple teaching. You would have needed no swords or cudgels to arrest me there, and yet you did not lay hands on me!" But this was no time for words.

This unexpected treachery on the part of one of their inner circle threw the other disciples into a panic. Peter was furious. Having a sword, he drew it frantically from his belt and attacked one of the soldiers and cut off the man's ear. When Jesus saw what had happened, he said quietly to Peter, "Put your sword back into your belt. All that take up the sword will perish with the sword."

Terrified and fearing that they, too, would be captured, every one of his disciples turned and ran away as fast as he could go, leaving Jesus alone with his captors. When they had bound him, they led him back into the city and to the palace of the High Priest where he was held as a prisoner.

Jesus' disciples, like sheep attacked by wolves and without a shepherd, had scattered, not knowing where to go. Peter was the first to recover his senses and to feel shame for having deserted his Master. In a few moments he was running back toward the garden to find the officers who were leading Jesus away. Peter followed after them as close behind as he dared. When he saw them going through the gateway to the High Priest's palace, he walked behind the officers, as far as the open courtyard.

Since there was quite a crowd already in the court — both men and women, servants as well as police officers — Peter thought he would not be recognized and perhaps he could find out what had happened to Jesus. Like others about him, he walked over to an open fire, and began warming his hands. As he stood there in the light of the fire, a maid came up to him, and looked suspiciously into his face, and said, "You were with Jesus, the Galilean, when he was captured, weren't you?"

But Peter denied it, saying, "I do not know what you are talking about." As soon as he dared, he walked away from the light of the fire into another part of the courtyard. But there another maid saw him, and in a superior tone of voice said to the others, "This man here was with Jesus of Nazareth." Again Peter denied it. "I swear I do not know the man."

Another person came up to Peter, and said: "You surely were one of that man's disciples. Your way of speaking gives you away as a Galilean."

Peter then became more positive. He swore again: "I do not know the man at all," and walked out of the courtyard where he would not be watched.

Presently the crowing of a rooster startled him. He had forgotten all about whether it was night or day. Nothing had seemed real until the rooster crowed. Then suddenly he remembered who he really was and how again and again he had told Jesus that he would never desert him. "Even though everyone else leaves you," he had said, "I will never leave you." And yet he, Peter, had denied, not just once, nor twice, but three times, that he had ever known Jesus. Peter wandered off alone, overcome with his shame, and wept bitterly.

In the meantime, the two police officers who were guarding Jesus found a mad satisfaction in tormenting their new prisoner. They made him stand up before them with feet bound together and with his hands tied behind his back. Then after blindfolding him, they began to tease him in mockery. One or another would strike him, and call "Tell us, great and mighty one, which of us struck you?" When Jesus did not speak, they laughed scornfully and beat him with their sticks.

Finally they returned him, bruised and aching, to his cell, and left him helpless on the floor for the rest of the night.

As soon as it was day, Caiaphas, the High Priest, summoned certain members of his official council to meet in the palace to help in preparing the written charges to be brought before Pilate, the Roman governor. After some discussion, they agreed on three. First, Jesus had been teaching the people things contrary to the laws of Moses. He had attempted to upset the temple ceremonies. He had said that he would even destroy the whole temple and in its place would put up another entirely different kind of temple. Such a rebel must be regarded as a threat to all leaders of the people, both Jewish and Roman.

Second, it was said that Jesus had forbidden his followers to pay the recent additional taxes demanded by the Romans. That was a step toward treason.

Third, there were many people who were openly saying that at last the Messiah had come — he who was to be the King of the Jews. Jesus' popularity with the masses was growing by leaps and bounds. If he should ever really become this great national leader, Pilate would have a dangerous rival with whom to contend.

When the group had agreed on the charges, Caiaphas ordered the prisoner brought before them for questioning. If he were to confess his guilt, their case would be certain. So Jesus, haggard and bruised, and with his hands still bound, was led into the room to face his accusers.

Addressing Jesus, Caiaphas said, "Tell us now, briefly, just what are the important things you have been teaching?"

"Your Honor," answered Jesus, "I have spoken openly to the world. I have been teaching in synagogues and in the temple. I have kept none of my teachings secret. Why, then, do you ask me what I have been teaching? Ask those who have heard me and learn from them what I have been saying."

One of the officers standing nearby struck him with his hand, saying, "Do you answer the High Priest so?"

Jesus said: "If I have spoken evil, tell me what is the evil; but if well, why have you struck me?"

The High Priest was insulted and shouted, "I command you by the living God that you tell us whether or not you are the Messiah!"

Jesus answered, "If I tell you, you will not believe me; if I ask

you a question, you will not answer." Then they all cried out together, "Are you the Messiah?" Jesus answered, "You are the
ones who are speaking of me as the Messiah. But those are not
my words."

Unable to get Jesus to confess Caiaphas ordered the prisoner
returned to his cell. The priests then once more went carefully
over their charges and adjourned, expecting to meet next in Pilate's Judgment Hall.

. . . .

Judas slipped quietly away from the garden where he had
accomplished Jesus' arrest, and wandered down into the Kedron
Valley, hardly knowing where he was going. He was struggling
with his conscience; he had to make himself believe he had done
right. When, long past midnight, he made his way back into the
city and to the home of one of his friends, he thought he had
settled the matter. As if nothing special had happened he lay down
beside his friend and tried to sleep, but his thoughts would not rest.
They fought with each other as two men in battle. Over and over
he saw himself running to kiss Jesus. Judas began to hate himself.
With each passing hour, his crime against his long-time friend grew
bigger and more detestable. He wished he had never been born.
He could not bear to live with the memory of his treachery to
haunt him.

He rose from his sleeping mat and, picking up the bag filled
with the pieces of silver, he stepped quietly out of the house and
went back to the Palace of the High Priest. The men of the
Sanhedrin were still sitting in the hall working on their statement
to Pilate. Judas surprised them by coming to the door. "Do you
wish more money?" asked the High Priest.

Judas answered by flinging the thirty pieces of silver on the
floor before them. "I have sinned!" he cried. "I have betrayed a
righteous man!"

"What is that to us?" answered the priests as if with one voice.

Then they turned again to their own business.

So Judas walked away, gloomy and silent. There was none to
pity him. Down into the valley and out beyond the city walls he
went alone. And there beneath a tree, in the dim, grey light before the dawn, he hanged himself.

19 The End

IN the early morning, while the city was still quiet, a messenger
went forth from the palace of Caiaphas, with a note to Pontius
Pilate. It said briefly, "We have just arrested the dangerous rebel,
Jesus the Galilean, of whom you have already heard many things.
We have prepared our charges and witnesses can be called quickly.
The case, as you well know, is urgent. We await your command."

Pilate was not one to delay long in disposing of rebels. Regardless of the fact that the celebration of the yearly Passover was
at its height, he ordered certain members of the priestly council
to assemble that very morning in the Hall of Judgment for the
prisoner's trial.

By this time, the people of the city were beginning to stir. Early
risers became curious on seeing a prisoner, with hands bound, being
led up the street from the palace of the High Priest toward the
palace of the Governor. Even those who had known Jesus did not
at first recognize him with his clothes torn and soiled and his head
bare. Could it be that the pallid and unwashed face and the bound
hands were those of the bold young man who two days before had
rebuked the money-changers and driven them out of the temple?
It was a shock to see him now — helpless and in disgrace. Men and
women, some frightened and weeping, others merely full of curi-

osity, came running up the hill toward Pilate's palace. Stopped by
the guards in front of the palace gate, they grew into a stormy mob.
They scarcely knew why they wanted to be there. They only knew
they could not stay away.

Pilate, the Governor, took his seat on the royal throne while
all in the court stood and bowed to do him honor. He read the
scroll handed to him by one of the priests. Then all eyes turned
toward the gateway and watched with solemn awe as the prisoner,
led by two Roman soldiers, walked into the court and stood before
the Governor.

Pilate then turned to the priests sitting on his right hand and
said, "I have read your charges. Now present your witnesses."

One witness after another spoke: "We have found this man
turning our people against the laws. He has been trying to change
our customs. He is upsetting the peace of our nation. He has said
he would destroy our temple, which you and Herod the Great before you have helped us to build through these many years. And
finally, he calls himself the Messiah, who will free our nation from
Your Majesty's rule. He claims that he is the true King of the
Jews."

On hearing these charges, Pilate turned to Jesus and said:
"Your own nation and your own priests have delivered you up to
me. Now tell me yourself what you have done? Have you been
saying that you are the true King of the Jews?"

Calmly Jesus answered Pilate: "The kingdom I have been
preaching is not a kingdom like yours, nor is it like any other kingdom of this world. It is not a kingdom that anyone can see. It has
no thrones nor palaces nor lands. Its king is God; and God rules in
the hearts of men."

"Do you call yourself a king, then?" asked Pilate, somewhat
mystified.

Jesus answered: "It is you and these priests who are calling me a king, not I. I have one desire only and that is to preach the things that are true."

Hearing these words, Pilate turned to the priests and said, "Judging from what he himself says, this man is not guilty of treason or rebellion. He has done nothing worthy of death."

On seeing Pilate weaken, Jesus' accusers pressed their arguments more vigorously. Different ones among them tried to speak, each scarcely waiting for the other to finish before he began.

"But he stirs up the people."

"He tells the people to disobey our laws."

"He has been preaching all over the country from Galilee to this place. Thousands are ready to do whatever he says."

"You have heard what happened in the temple just two days ago. That was just a beginning of what he would do. We have uncovered a plot to destroy the temple."

All the while, outside the gate, the crowd became noisier. Some shouted, "Release our Jesus!" Others called for his death. Pilate saw that Jesus had both loyal friends and strong enemies. The proofs against the prisoner were none too good, to be sure, but Pilate was no stickler for justice. The safety of his own throne was more important than one person's life. Jesus would not be the first man Pilate had crucified in order to put terror into the hearts of would-be rebels. Even that morning he had already sentenced two thieves to that cruel punishment.

Such were some of Pilate's thoughts as he sat watching and listening. The voices of Jesus' enemies seemed to be drowning out the voices of his friends. Pilate saw that if he ordered the crucifixion of the prisoner he would not need to fear an uprising.

Pilate made his decision. In a stern voice he pronounced the sentence of death on Jesus of Galilee and commanded that he be crucified.

Immediately the two guards standing beside Jesus led him away to another room. There they and others with them began to ridi-

"I have only one desire
and that is to preach the things that are true."

cule and torment Jesus. With stinging laughter, they put a purple robe on him. They placed a crown of thorns on his head and gave him a rod to hold in his right hand as a royal sceptre. With pretended dignity, they then kneeled down before him and cried, "Hail! King of the Jews!" They ended their mock ceremony by spitting in his face. Taking off his royal robe, they again put on his own clothes and began beating him with a whip — blow upon blow. During all their torturing, Jesus did not open his mouth or show any sign of anger.

The sad news of Jesus' fate traveled swiftly from friend to friend in the city. By the time the trial was over, a large crowd had gathered outside the castle grounds. They could do nothing else than be by his side even though they knew it would break their hearts to see him. So, many people were waiting beside the castle gate when three condemned men were led out. At the sight of Jesus, bowed down like the other two men, under the heavy weight of the cross he was made to carry over his shoulder, the people broke down and wailed pitifully. Up through the narrow and winding streets the throng followed, trying to press close to Jesus to let him know that there were those who cared and were willing to share his suffering. Slowly the sorrowful procession moved along out through the gate in the city wall, and across the valley to a barren hillside north of Jerusalem where crosses often stood against the sky.

By midday three new crosses were lifted up, with the brave and adored Jesus nailed and tied to the cross in the center. On his drooping head lay the crown of thorns with which the soldiers had mocked him. Nailed above his head was a sign that read: "This is the King of the Jews" — a cruel and lying jibe at a dying man and a public insult to all Jewish national hopes.

Even during these last hours of agony, a small group of Jesus' friends remained at his side, trying to ease his pain and listening for his faintest words. A Roman captain in charge of the tragic work overheard Jesus pray even in his suffering and say, "Father, forgive them, for they know not what they do." The soldier was amazed at the tenderness of Jesus' prayer. Afterwards, as he told his comrades the story of Jesus' behavior, he said, "Surely, this was a righteous man!"

By mid-afternoon, before the sun had set behind the western hills, the deadly work was finished. Jesus was gone. Only his body hung on the cross.

How speedily it had all happened! Just the evening before, Jesus' twelve disciples had eaten the Passover supper with him. His friends were still too dazed by the shock to believe the truth. They had been hoping for great things of Jesus. He had been to them like a bright light in the darkness. But now the light had been cruelly snuffed out. They were terrified at the horror of it. In the agony of their despair, they cried out, "Why, why, O God, could you not have saved him?" But no answer came to their crying. The very daylight seemed suddenly turned to darkness.

When word went out that death had finally come, one of Jesus' old friends, Joseph of Arimathaea, went at once to Pilate and asked if he might be given the right to take the body down from the cross and bury it. When permission was given, Joseph was joined by another faithful friend, Nicodemus, a Pharisee. Together, the two men carried the precious body to a lovely garden not far off, that Joseph owned, where there was a private vault in which no other corpse had yet been laid. The two men bathed the body with perfumes and sprinkled it with sweet-scented spices they had brought, and wrapped it in clean linen cloths. With loving hearts they laid it away in a stone coffin; with a large stone slab that had been hewn to fit the doorway, they closed the vault. All they could do for their Master was ended. With aching and heavy hearts, they walked away.

20 The End Becomes the Beginning

THE remaining eleven disciples and the good women who had been accustomed to travel about with Jesus returned to Galilee brokenhearted. In their grief they clung to one another for comfort. They gathered in each other's homes and tried to talk. They were struggling to understand why God had allowed Jesus to be killed. Surely one so sincerely right with God, so overflowing in good will, did not deserve the punishment due a criminal or rebel. Why had God forsaken one so righteous?

For many days, no one could find an answer to these tormenting questions. It was as if the foundation stones on which these men and women had built their beliefs had been blasted out from under them. They were left shaken as by an earthquake. As they tried to look toward the future, they could see nothing but desolation. They had hoped that Jesus would save their nation in some way — they did not know how, but somehow he would be their deliverer. Now his voice was forever stilled. The Roman conquerors were too powerful even for him. "He saved others; himself he could not save."

But slowly a strange thing began to happen. As these men and women gathered day after day in each other's homes, they began to recall the wonderful experiences they had had with Jesus. They told one another of happenings they had almost forgotten. The very tone of Jesus' voice and the look on his face would come back to them so vividly that it seemed sometimes as though Jesus were again right there with them.

In addition to these experiences together, some had dreams in which Jesus came back and talked with them. In these dreams, Jesus seemed so real that the dreamers could not tell whether they

158

had been asleep or awake when they saw him. Some declared positively that they had seen Jesus again. He had talked with them. They were sure of it. The rumor spread that Jesus had actually come out of his coffin, that Peter and John had seen him, and that several of the women also had talked with him; they would see him only for a few moments, and then he would mysteriously disappear again. Finally, several of them dreamed they saw Jesus rise up from the earth — higher and higher — until he disappeared entirely. They believed he had gone to heaven to be with God. And after that their dreams of seeing him and talking with him stopped.

But for these men and women to believe that God had brought Jesus back to life in this way after he had been killed made a tremendous impression. It changed even their memories of him. They believed as never before that Jesus was a Man of God, that he was different from other men. Perhaps his being killed, they said, was after all part of God's plan. But what could that plan have been? It took time for them to work it all out, but some of them did. They decided that Jesus was truly the savior for whose coming they had been yearning, but that he was a savior for all the world, not for the Jews alone. They believed also that Jesus would actually come back again to live on this earth. He would come down from heaven through the clouds, and he would set up a great world kingdom. Jesus would become king of kings and lord of lords. The great dreams of the prophets for world-wide peace and righteousness would then come true.

But the years passed by. The men and women who knew Jesus died. Their children and their children's children also died. But Jesus did not come back. Nearly two thousand years have come and gone. Still Jesus has not come back. There are those who are still hoping for his second coming.

But others believe that this Jesus, the carpenter's son, will never live again on the earth. What has been handed down to us from generation to generation regarding his life is the world's great treasure. His spirit never needs to die. When he lived on the earth, only small groups could listen to his words. Today his teachings are heard and his story is told weekly in thousands of houses of worship. At first but a small circle of friends tried to spread his message. Now the followers of Jesus are numbered by the millions. They live in every land. They speak all languages. Just as a grain of wheat falls into the ground and dies, yet from it there grows a new plant that bears new fruit and new seeds, so was Jesus' death. And so, he taught, the Kingdom of God would grow. And so the Kingdom of God continues to grow.

> "The strong men keep coming on,
> They go down shot, hanged, sick, broken. . . .
>
> .   .   .   .
>
> Call hallelujah, call amen, call deep thanks.
> The strong men keep coming on."[1]

---

[1]Carl Sandburg, "Upstream," *Slabs of the Sunburnt West* (New York: Harcourt, Brace & Co., Inc., 1922).

Biblical Sources